AMERICA'S NATIONAL PARKS: HOW WELL DO YOU KNOW THEM?

STAY SAFE! . . . . STAY HOME IN AMERICA! . . . . VISIT YOUR PARKS!

365 Days . . . 388 Ways to Experience America

Questions, Answers, and Sidebars by:

KENNETH MICHAEL BROPHY

Kennett

ELDERBERRY PRESS, INC.
1393 Old Homestead Drive, Second Floor
Oakland, Oregon 97462-9506.
E-MAIL: editor@elderberrypress. com
TEL/FAX: 541. 459. 6043
www. elderberrypress. com

Publisher's Catalog-in-Publication Data
America's National Parks: How Well Do You Know Them?
/Kenneth Brophy
ISBN 1-932762-14-0
1. National Parks.
2. Quiz Book.
3. Trivia.
4. Tour Book.
5. Tour Guide.
I. Title
This book was written, printed and bound in the United
States of America.

In Memory

This book is dedicated to all those
Who lost their lives for
FREEDOM

America under attack.
September 11th, 2001

It is equally dedicated to all those
Who preserve and protect
Our National Parks . . .

The Park Rangers

CONTENTS

CHAPTER 1 -
INTRODUCTION

In 1916, the United States Government created the National Park Service (NPS), under the auspice of the Department of the Interior, and assigned it the mountainous task of protecting, improving and preserving America's National Parks for future generations of Americans to enjoy. In those early days, the number of parks falling under the NPS protective wing was less than 50.Today, the number of national park sites that "the National Park Service administers for the enjoyment of the people" has grown to 388[1] areas - including national seashores, wild rivers, memorials, historic places, battlefields, trails and scenic parks. The NPS proudly, and deservingly, refers to these areas as "treasures of our nation . . . incredibly diverse, the parks range from well-known areas of natural beauty such as Yellowstone and the Grand Canyon to historic Independence Hall and to lesser-known areas commemorating presidents, decisive battles and famous Americans from all walks of life".

In 1986, in an attempt to encourage and promote visitation to the parks, the National Park Service introduced the national parks passport program. This highly successful program made available to the public, for a small fee, a NPS passport book – Passport To Your National Parks (referred to herein as "Passport") – which is a valuable, compact and handy guide to all 388 national park sites. Under the direction of the NPS, Eastern National Park and Monument Association, a non-profit organization, designed, collected the information and published Passport to serve as a traveling companion to visitors at each park. Inside Passport is a condensed, color-coded map detailing where each park can be found within the vast NPS system. Passport is divided into nine geographical travel regions and one trail system segment. America's National Parks: How Well Do You Know Them? has been organized in the same geographic manner.

Passport also contains a brief description of each park and a place to record your visit, i.e., date and park name, via a Passport cancellation stamp unique to each site. A visitor center is located at most parks, where you can view an informative slide presentation, take in a museum with hands-on educational displays, browse a bookstore with site-specific literature, and, more importantly to some, collect your Passport cancellation stamp. In the words of Eastern National, "These cancellations allow you the opportunity to share and relive your journey through America's national parks. Passport will become a valuable and informative scrapbook to cherish for years."

If you don't already have a Passport, I suggest you get one . . . in my opinion it is the best and, perhaps, the healthiest investment money can buy. Then get out, see America, see our jewels, bring your family and friends, bring your Passport, collect all 388 cancellations and a few wonderful, lasting memories in the process. As the great American conservationist John Muir said, "A thousand Yellowstone wonders are calling, look up and down and round about you!"

To help you enjoy your visit, thousands of devoted NPS employees, volunteers and non-profit organization staff administer the parks, 24 hours a day – every day of the year. These people represent all walks of life, e.g., biologists, research scientists, interpreters, law enforcement officers, chefs, waiters and waitresses, educators, photographers, maintenance personnel, clerks and accountants, to name just a few. Perhaps the most important service provider, however, is that American icon – the Park Ranger. In their simple, but elegant, uniform with its distinctive hat, the Park Rangers greet all visitors with an air of comfort and confidence, patiently answering questions, interpreting nature and other unique park highlights, and guiding patrons through the park. They come to work to give; what they offer is themselves . . . their knowledge and talents. Together, they provide valuable and worthwhile services, which include Ranger-led snowshoe day-trips and interpreter nature walks, camp-fire programs, slide shows, research assistance, technical hike and climbing advice, and conduct other educational programs. They also oversee the work of support and volunteer agencies that provide hospitality services, from fast food cafeterias to campsite and serene overnight lodging.

Beware – some journeys to distant park sites can take days and involve several modes of transportation, e.g., auto, air, train or bus, canoe or kayak, and sometimes lots of walking. America's National Parks: How Well Do You Know Them? is a collection of questions that is meant to accompany you on your journey, to provide a source of site-specific material of educational and entertainment value. The book's plethora of questions, with accompanying answers, is intended to stimulate pre-site visit interest and encourage post-site visit research. All 388 sites are represented by at least one question in the book. Questions range in scope from art, poetry, natural phenomena, nature, wild life, geology, geography, history, myth, botany, to anthropology. So as you travel America's roads, rivers and byways, place <u>America's National Parks: How Well Do You Know Them?</u> on your lap beside your maps, compass, tourist brochures and GPS, and refer to it for entertainment, relaxation, or to break up the monotony of hours-and-hours and miles-and-miles of travel. Use it to test your knowledge and that of your traveling companions – it's possible you may learn something new, too.

As the NPS recommends, buy an annual National Parks Pass (for about $50) which entitles you and your family to admission at all parks requiring entry fees . . . "Remember you have 365 days and 388 ways to experience **Your** America." Have Fun!

<u>Footnote(s):</u>
1.   A list of all 388 sites, provided by the National Park Service, is included as Appendix A.

Introduction

The map of the United States below is divided into the same nine geographical regions as the NPS uses to manage and administer the parks. Each region is covered by a separate chapter in this book.

4. Pacific Northwest & Alaska

9. Rocky Mtn.

7. Midwest

10. North Atlantic

11. Mid Atlantic

5. Western

6. Southeast

8 Southwest

North Atlantic Region
Mid-Atlantic Region
National Capital Region
Southeast Region
Midwest Region
Southwest Region
Rocky Mountain Region
Western Region
Pacific Northwest and Alaska Regions

4 Pacific

5. Western - Hawaii & Guam

Chapter	NPS Region	Chapter	NPS Region
3	National Capital	8	Southwest
4	Pacific Northwest and Alaska	9	Rocky Mountain
5	Western	10	North Atlantic
6	Southeast	11	Mid-Atlantic
7	Midwest		

CHAPTER 2 -
NATIONAL PARK SERVICE – SYSTEM-WIDE

The National Park Service provides colorful, informative brochures
(above) at each of the 388 NPS sites across America. Brochures fold
out to include distinguishing photos, detailed maps, elaborate diagrams
and interesting narratives about the natural and historical aspects of
each park. They are available at the park entrance or visitor center. Just
ask a Ranger, they're free!

CHAPTER 2 -
NATIONAL PARK SYSTEM – SYSTEM WIDE
Questions

Chapter 2 is your first avalanche of questions meant to enlighten, entertain and measure your knowledge of the overall NPS system.

Enjoy the questions and have fun! (Answers are found at the end of each Chapter.)

1   Which statement best describes a NPS motto?
   A. Take only what you can safely carry.
   B. Take only those plants you can transplant and grow at home.
   C. Take only one plant, rock, seashell or animal per person.
   D. Leave only footprints, take only memories.

2   "The best idea America ever had", said Wallace Stegner, winner of the Pulitzer Prize, when he learned of America's allotment of its first national park. Name America's first national Park, the president who authorized it, and the year?

3   Which national park occupies the largest area and, in fact, is considered the largest national park in the World?

4   In the aftermath of a costly Civil War, Americans dubbed the purchase of this property "Seward's Folly", after Secretary of State William Seward. What property did Seward buy for $7.2 million in 1867?

5   Park Rangers and visitors alike battle only two seasons in Alaska. What are the two seasons?

6   When was the National Park Service established and who was the first NPS Director?

7   To what US government agency does the NPS report?

8   This national park has been designated a desert biosphere by the United Nations . . . name it.

9   The National Park Service logo is a picturesque emblem with silhouettes of a giant sequoia tree, a lonesome buffalo and snowcapped Mount Rainier. Man is not present. What does the logo shape represent?

10   The importance of a biosphere is to:
    A. Allow the United Nations unlimited access to the site and exclusive hunting privileges for UN members.
    B. Preserve an area in its pristine state to permit future environmental studies and comparisons.
    C. Promote an area for biological research.
    D. Allow the United Nations to share in revenues collected at the site to benefit research.

11   This national park has been designated a boreal forest biosphere. Hint: It exists on a northern island.

12   This national park has the highest land elevation . . . name it.

13   This national park has the lowest land elevation in the Western Hemisphere . . . name the park and its lowest elevation.

14   The National Park Service wants visitors to have a pleasant, safe visit, and to assist in protecting the parks and their wildlife for the future. In doing so, the NPS wants visitors to obey which of the following rules:
    A. Keep wildlife wild by not feeding them.
    B. Give wildlife lots of space, don't get close to them; if they feel threatened they are aggressive and dangerous, and they can carry rabies, bubonic plaque, and Lyme disease or Rocky Mountain spotted fever.
    C. Keep pets home, they are not allowed on trails.
    D. All of the above.

15   What is the largest living thing on the planet and where can it be found?

16   What is the tallest living thing on the planet and where can it be found?

17   Name the two national parks that are the furthest distance from the 48 States.

18   Decide whether the statements below are true or false:
A. The National Park System offers many wonderful opportunities for viewing wildlife; most of these are easily accessible by road or trial. _____
B. There are over 500 National Wildlife Refuge Preserves in America. _____
C. For security reasons, wildlife viewing is banned at US Military bases. _____
D. Wildlife viewing brings refreshment of body and mind._____

19   A sign at Denali National Park visitor center reads, "95% of visitors see a grizzly bear, but only 5% of visitors see . . ." What is it that only 5% of visitors see?

20   Which is the newest park to join the ranks of the NPS?

21   This natural landmark helped steer the pioneer wagon trains west? What is it?

22   What State is the only one in America that does not have a national park site?

23   This artist immigrated to America from Switzerland and set up a photo-portrait studio in New Jersey. As a young man, he contracted with the US government to "go west" and paint the beautiful scenery of Yellowstone, Yosemite Valley and the Rocky Mountains. He train-ed and burro-ed to each site (before they became national parks), took elaborate photos using the best available technology of the time – large, bulky metal plates – and returned to his studio to develop the negatives and

paint spectacular oil landscapes (some 6 feet x 8 feet). His art hangs in the National Gallery of Art – West Wing – the National Museum of American Art, both in Washington, DC (WDC), and the National Cowboy Hall of Fame and Western Heritage Center, Oklahoma City, Oklahoma. He is best known for his paintings 'The Last Buffalo' and 'Emigrants Crossing the Plains'. Name the artist.

A. Walt Disney
B. Norman Rockwell
C. Albert Bierstadt
D. Winslow Homer

Sidebar – 'The Last Buffalo' is a powerful, magnificent and moving painting. My eyes swelled with tears when I first saw it. The artist traveled by train throughout the great American prairies and witnessed, firsthand, the unnecessary slaughter of the buffalo. His painting is a tribute to the buffalo and the Native Americans ["Indians"] who were dependent on it for food, clothing, implements, jewelry and shelter. In the foreground, an Indian on horseback is shown stabbing a lance into the side of a buffalo, while the buffalo is shown with its head under the horse and horns stabbing the belly of the horse, lifting the horse and throwing the Indian to the ground. The background depicts miles of buffalo raging toward the viewer with dead horses, Indians and buffalo scattered here and there.

'Emigrants Crossing the Plains' depict a wagon train at dusk about to circle the wagons for the evening.

24   Which park receives the most visitors per annum?

25   Which park receives the fewest visitors per annum?

26   The average time a visitor spends at one of the NPS sites is:
A. One hour
B. Four hours
C. One day
D. One week

27   This site houses the oldest structure preserved and protected by the NPS. Name the site.

28   For the most part, Park Rangers are educated, knowledgeable, pleasant, unselfish, helpful, good-natured and obliging. Most are college graduates. What college degree is most common among park rangers?
        A.   Bachelor of Science
        B.   Bachelor of Arts
        C.   Business degree
        D.   Law degree

29   The following prose pays tribute to America's scenery found throughout the nation's parks:
                "Whose woods these are I think I know,
                His house is in the village though . . .
                My horse must think it queer,
                To stop without a farmhouse near . . .
                Miles to go before I sleep, and
                Miles to go before I sleep."
        What is the name of the poem, and who is this great American poet, winner of four Pulitzer Prizes?

30   This memorial, at 555 feet, is the nation's tallest monument. Name the monument.

31   As used by the NPS, the term "Rebound" is best described by the following:
        A.   The remains of a snow avalanche.
        B.   The action of rocks that break off mountains because of wind, temperature and water erosion, and they, in turn, bounce in all directions.
        C.   After a herd of buffalo spend the night on the prairie, the native grasses slowly regain position upright.
        D.   Over vast geological time, removal of glaciers slowly causes land to uplift.

32   Abraham Lincoln, 16th president of the United States, is buried
      here:
      A. Beneath the Lincoln Memorial, WDC
      B. Lincoln Home National Historic Site, Springfield,
          Illinois
      C. Lincoln Boyhood National Memorial, Lincoln City,
          Kentucky
      D. Arlington National Cemetery, across the Potomac
          River and directly in line with the Lincoln Memorial,
          the Washington Monument and the Capital Building.

33   This great president said, "There is nothing so American as our
      National Parks. The fundamental idea behind the parks is . . .
      that the country belongs to the people . . . making for the
      enrichment of the lives of all of us. The parks stand as the
      outward symbol of this great human principle." Which
      president said that?

34   What Secretary of the Interior was given the nickname, "I-
      Don't-Like-To-Hike."

35   When "I-Don't-Like-To-Hike" Watt suggested to the nation his
      intention to open up 130 million acres of land and 16 off-shore
      oil sites, he was met at the steps of the state capitol in Juneau,
      Alaska with __?__. What met Watt (pardon the pun)?

36   What is the oldest living thing in the national park service?

37   Considered the father of modern conservation movement, this
      talented author prepared a report for the NPS; in it he
      recommended a wilderness management policy that the NPS
      adopted and still uses today. Name the author.

38   In 1956 Congress named this tree America's National Shrine. It
      is our National Christmas Tree and a living memorial to all
      U.S. war dead. An annual Christmas service is held at the tree,
      and a wreath is placed there to honor the dead. At 267.4 feet it
      is the third tallest tree in the world. It is 2,000 years old. Name
      the tree and the national park where it lives.

39   Following World War II, the NPS abandoned the practice of naming trees. This no-name tree was measured and found to be 17 feet dbh. For what is dbh an abbreviation?

40   There are 750 bird species in North America; the majority of them can be found in our national parks. Name any ten. Hint: Most home bird-feeders see 20 to 25 species. Sea-gull is not a species.

41   Aldo Leopold, a talented scientist, poet and forest management expert, bought a sick, worn-out farm in Wisconsin, and over a few years restored and nursed it back to health. He kept a daily journal about the experience and latter converted it into a book. The New York Public Library's book, <u>Books of the (20th) Century</u>, includes Leopold's book in its list of the 100 best books. Many consider it the best nature book of all time. Name the book.

42   America has many types of wetlands that are dispersed throughout the NPS sites. Which statement best describes a wetland:
    A.   Wetlands are areas between land and water bodies, where water periodically floods the land or saturates the soil.
    B.   Wetlands include mangroves, marshes, swamps, bogs, fens and estuaries.
    C.   Moose, flamingos, anhinga, bald eagles, roseate spoon-bill, beaver and alligators, to name a few, depend upon wetlands for their survival – More than half of America's wetlands have vanished to development.
    D.   Wetlands produce annually 50% more bio-mass then any other plant community.
    E.   All of the above.

43   Which statement concerning hypothermia is false?
      A. Occurs when the body loses heat faster than it can
          produce it.
      B. Hypothermia takes more lives each year than any
          other outdoor hazard.
      C. Hypothermia only occurs in the winter
      D. As blood is diverted to vital organs, hands and feet
          become numb, resulting in uncontrollable shivering,
          fumbling, and drowsiness, followed by stupor,
          collapse and death.

44   "A lake is a landscape's most beautiful and
          expressive feature." Henry David Thoreau.

      With 35 lakes, this national park has the most lakes . . .
      name it.

45   In 1990, 13 wildlife-conscious organizations met in
      Washington, D.C. to sign a memorandum of understanding
      pledging to carry out a "Watchable Wildlife Program". The
      program has grown to great success with over 500 wildlife
      viewing stations, platforms and visitor centers in America
      today. The U.S. Fish and Wildlife Service, Bureau of
      Reclamation, U.S. Forest Service, National Audubon Society
      and U.S. Army are a few of the organizations to join the
      "Watchable Wildlife Program". Name three other organizations
      that signed the memorandum of understanding.

46   Which of the following is **not** a goal of the "Watchable Wildlife
      Program":
      A. Bring wildlife close enough for children to pet them
          and hunters to shoot them.
      B. Enhance wildlife viewing opportunities.
      C. Provide education about wildlife and its needs.
      D. Promote active support of wildlife conservation.

47   "What draws us into the desert is the
      search for something intimate in the remote."
              Edward Abby, Desert Solitaire

Name four deserts in the National Park System where you can
experience the ". . . intimate in the remote."

48   What percent of the earth's land surface is desert?

49   Great men rise to create great programs to combat great
      depressions. During the Great Depression of 1933, President
      Franklin Delano Roosevelt conceived a program to put
      thousands of Americans back to work, by building projects for
      the NPS. Roosevelt's forces built buildings and monuments,
      hiking trials and visitor centers, levees and weirs to create
      wetland wildlife refuges for millions of birds, and roads
      through remote areas and over impassable mountains. They
      were given room and board and paid $1 per day. What was this
      ambitious program called?

50   Crustose, fruticose and foliose are organisms found throughout
      the NPS – from the forests of New England, to the sea-floor
      deserts of the Southwest; from the rocky shores of Maine, to
      the sandy cliffs of the California coast; from the 'lake islands'
      of Superior, to the 'sky islands' of Chricahua. This organism
      brightens the landscape in pastel colors of yellow, green and
      orange. Name the family of organisms.

51   "He lives contentedly if he has
      only that which nature provides."
              Father Ignaz Pfefferkorn, 1736

The NPS has been tasked by Congress to protect and preserve
the national parks and their resources for the future. A
'grandfather clause', however, protects certain Native
Americans, granting them the right within America's national
park lands to carry on age-old customs of 'living off the land',
thus, to continue to hunt caribou, harpoon Beluga whale, club
walrus for tusk/ivory carving, fish and harvest wood, wild
berries, mushrooms, plants and roots. Inuits in Alaska continue

to harpoon Beluga whales at Prudhoe Bay and shoot caribou herds as they swim across Onion Portage, Kobuk Valley NP, Alaska. Natives are even permitted to slaughter walrus and take their ivory tusks (canine teeth) for carving handicrafts. What is this practice called?

52 Geologically, the three main categories of rock found in the NPS parks are _____, _____, and _____. Name them.

53 Prehistoric cave paintings and rock carvings are known as _____. What are they called?

54 My face is peeling, sheets of rock are falling off, and thin flakes of slate shed from freeze-thaw, hot-cold, and wet-dry conditions. What is this disease, these geologic phenomena from which I suffer?

55 Why are trees referred to as the "lung tissue" of the earth?

56 Is it still possible to explore virgin "old-growth" forests on the East Coast?   Yes or no?

57 Through care, dedication and research, the NPS has successfully reintroduced 140 river otters, peregrine falcon nesting pairs, and native brook trout at this national park. Name the national park.

58 What is the purpose of the NPS' "Bloomin' Report"?

59 What is the oldest living tree species east of the Mississippi River?

60 Somes Sound is the only fjord in the contiguous lower 48 states. Name the park in which it resides.

61 During the 1950's, park visitor centers were created as part of an ambitious post-war program launched by Conrad Wirth under a scheme popular at the time called _____? What was Wirth's scheme called, and what else did the scheme finance?

CHAPTER 2 -
NATIONAL PARK SERVICE – SYSTEM WIDE
Answers

1   Correct answer is D; 'Leave No Trace' is the NPS outdoor ethic policy. It's a good policy that ensures the preservation of our parks for future generations.

2   Yellowstone became not only America's first, but also the world's first national park. It was authorized by President Grant in 1872. It was designated a biosphere by the United Nations Educational Scientific and Cultural Organization (UNESCO) in 1976, and a World Heritage Site in 1996.

3   Wrangle – St. Elias NP and Preserve, Alaska, which, according to America's Spectacular National Parks, 1999, edited by Letitia Burns O'Connor and Dana Levy, occupies over 20,000 square miles – uninhabited and, in places, still unexplored. According to Letitia and Dana, "It is six times the size of Yellowstone and larger than the States of New Hampshire and Vermont combined."

4   Alaska – Thank our lucky stars he did!

5   Winter and July

6   1916, Steven T. Mather

7   Department of the Interior

8   Organ Pipe Cactus NP located in the Sonora Desert, southwestern corner of Arizona.

9   A Native American arrowhead.

10   B is the correct answer

11   Isle Royale NP

12   Mount McKinley, Denali NP in Alaska at 20,320-ft above sea
      level, more than qualifies.
      Sidebar - Mt McKinley is the highest peak in the United States
      and North America.

13   Death Valley NP, California with an elevation -282 feet below
      sea level.

14   Correct answer is D

15   The giant Sequoia Tree; Sequoia NP, California.
      Sidebar - It is not, however, the tallest. That prize goes to the
      Redwood tree.

16   The Coastal Redwood Tree; Redwood NP, California.

17   War in the Pacific National Historical Park, Guam, and
      National Park of American Samoa are approximately 6,000
      miles west of the coast of California.

18   A = True, B = True, C = False, D = True.

19   Mount McKinley, because it is covered in clouds 300 days of
      the year.

20   Flight 93 National Memorial, Shanksville, Pennsylvania.

21   Chimney Rock NHS, Nebraska — an affiliated area with the
      Nebraska State Historical Society.

22   Delaware.

23   Correct answer is C – Bierstadt's paintings inspired people to
      visit the west, and aided Congress in obtaining the needed
      support to dedicate these areas as national parks.

24   Yosemite NP in California would be my guess.

25   Saint Croix Island HIS between Maine and Canada would be my guess.

26   Correct answer is B, four hours. From <u>America's Spectacular National Parks</u>.

27   Indian dwelling in the southeast, The Petroglyph NM at 12,000 years.

28   Correct answer is B.

29   'Stopping by the Woods on a Snowy Evening,' by Robert Frost.

30   (George) Washington Monument, WDC.

31   Correct answer is D.

32   Correct answer is B; Lincoln is buried on his own property, next to his wife and sons.

33   Franklin Delano Roosevelt . . . visit the FDR Memorial in WDC and learn more.

34   James Watt, Secretary of the Interior under President Reagan.

35   Watt was met with a twenty-one "chain-saw" salute.

36   Bristlecone pine trees at Great Basin NP, Nevada: one is estimated to be about 4,950-years old.

37   Aldo Leopold,
Sidebar – Leopold recommended protecting road-less wilderness areas from future development and urged the removal of recreation facilities that compromise park values, such as golf courses, ski lifts, and motorboat marinas. He was the first to advocate allowing natural fires to run their course because they clear out the forest, prairies and savannas, making room for new growth. He eloquently articulated the opinion that hunting should be banned in parks and, in its place, demonstrated the importance of predators in a healthy

National Park Service
System Wide

ecosystem; he said, ". . . hunting was a slow, crude tool compared to the precision instrument of predation that has shaped wildlife populations for millennia.", i.e., wolves, coyotes, fox, lynx, bears, jaguar, bobcat, mountain lions, owls, raptors, etc.. Ironically, Aldo was killed while helping to put out a prairie fire.

38   General Grant – Giant Sequoia Tree – Sequoia NP, California.

39   Diameter at Breast Height – a person measuring the diameter of a tree does so at breast height to avoid erroneous data caused by root interference.

40   You're on your own. Extra credit if you can name 25. Stop at any park visitor center and check your answer against a NPS bird book.

41   A Sand County Almanac.
         Sidebar – Stewart L. Udall, eight-year Secretary of the Interior, said, "Leopold wrote with the knowledge of a scientist and the eye of a poet". Leopold's Almanac is available at most libraries in audio cassette. Suggest listening to it rather than reading it . . . Udall does a great job of 'the read'.

42   Correct answer is E.

43   Correct answer is C – Death by hypothermia occurs in the summer when wetness and wind compound the effects of cool air. Hikers at higher elevations are particularly vulnerable if caught in a rain storm without proper protective clothing.

44   Isle Royale NP – An island!

45   U.S. Navy, U.S. Air Force, Bureau of Land Management, National Wildlife Federation, Izaak Walton League, International Association of Fish and Wildlife Agencies, Defenders of Wildlife, and the National Park Service.

National Park Service
System Wide

46   Correct answer is A.
      Sidebar – Children should never touch a wild animal, for they
      can be dangerous and carry diseases that can be transmitted to
      humans . . . hunting is not allowed at Watchable Wildlife Sites.

47   Mojave, Great Basin, Sonora and Chihuahuan Deserts, Western
      and Southwestern NPS Regions.

48   Twenty percent.

49   Civil Conservation Corps (CCC).
      Sidebar - Started in 1933, it remained in force until 1942.
      Noteworthy CCC projects include monuments at Great Smoky
      Mountains NP, the Appalachian Trial, visitor centers at
      Yellowstone and Yosemite NP's, hiking trials at Chiricahua NM
      and Cuyahoga Valley NRA, Trail Ridge road over the top of
      Rocky Mountain NP, and the many dikes, levees, weirs and
      other water control structures impounding 7,000 acres of water
      to create Seney National Wildlife Refuge – now home to
      hundreds of endangered trumpeter swans, nesting bald eagles
      and playful river otters . . . A GREAT PLACE TO VISIT!

50   Lichens.

51   Subsistence Privilege.

52   Metamorphic, sedimentary and igneous – volcanic.

53   Petroglyphs.
     Sidebar – Best parks to see petroglyphs first-hand are
     Petroglyph NM, Albuquerque, New Mexico; Bandelier NM,
     Los Alamos, New Mexico; Saguaro NP, Tucson, Arizona; and
     Canyon de Chelly NM, Chinle, Arizona.

54   Exfoliation.

55   During photosynthesis tree leaves combine sunlight with green
     chlorophyll, sugar and carbon, and in the process give off
     oxygen.

56   Yes, as much as one-forth of the acreage at Great Smoky
     Mountains NP is virgin forest.

57   Great Smoky Mountains NP, North Carolina and Tennessee

58   It chronicles weekly wildflower first-bloom sightings.

59   Blackgum Tree at Great Smokey Mountains NP is 564 years
     old.
     Sidebar - With a 257-inch circumference, it takes six people
     holding hands to encircle it.

60   Acadia NP, Bar Harbor, Maine.

61   Writh's hallmark scheme was known as "Mission 66" (A
     takeoff on the popular TV show Route 66). Besides visitor
     centers with interpretive exhibits and audio-visual programs, it
     funded parking lots, camp grounds with campfire circles,
     comfort stations and amphitheaters.

CHAPTER 3 -
NATIONAL CAPITAL REGION
Questions

These stamps picture the famous "Beardless Lincoln" portrait by Healy, the beloved statute in the Lincoln Memorial by French, a Lincoln-Douglas debate scene from an old print, and the rugged beard of Lincoln by Borglum.

1   Work began on this national memorial when the cornerstone was laid in 1848, but was discontinued when money ran out in 1853. Work was resumed in 1876 and finished in 1884. Name this prominent monument. Hint: It honors a president whom Col. Henry "Lighthorse" Lee described as, "First in war, first in peace, and first in the hearts of his countrymen."

2   Colonel Henry Lee was nicknamed "Lighthorse Harry". Why was he so nicknamed and who was his famous son?

3   Lincoln Memorial houses the famous 19-ft statue of Abe Lincoln, which was designed by Daniel Chester French. From what material did the sculptors, the Piccirilli brothers of New York, carve the statue?

4   Renowned architect Henry Bacon designed 36 Greek-revival columns to surround the Lincoln Memorial. What do they represent?

5   A lesser-known memorial to this great president, complete with a reflecting pool and statue, exists between the US Capitol Building and the Lincoln Memorial. Name this presidential memorial.

6   Visitors to the Franklin Delano Roosevelt Memorial are graciously guided through four outdoor rooms. What is the symbolism of the four rooms?

7   Which statement is true?
     A.   The US Capitol Building once had a copper dome.
     B.   Lincoln ordered construction on the US Capitol building to continue during the Civil War.
     C.   Two extension wings were added to the Capitol building and completed in 1863, before construction of the Washington Monument was complete.
     D.   All of the above.

8   The White House is the president's home and office, and the center of what branch of the government?

9   How did the president's home become known by the nickname 'The White House'?

10   The Red Room, Blue Room, Green Room, China Room, State Room, East Room and Vermeil Room can all be found inside this national public building.

11   The oldest public building in Washington is?

12   Every president except one lived in the White House. Name that one president.

13   This library in our nation's capitol contains 10,000 tulips flown in each year from Holland for spring planting. Each bulb is hand-planted, and usually blooms about the time the cherry blossoms are at their peak – the first week of April. Name the library.

14   This veteran's monument set aside a memorial dedicated to women, designed by a woman, Maya Ying Lin, to pay tribute to the dedication and ultimate sacrifice – death – women gave to this conflict. Name the memorial.

15   This war memorial depicts the moment when Marines raised a flag over Mount Suribachi, Iwo Jima. It inspired renewed patriotism when firefighters in NYC raised a flag in a similar manner over ground zero. Name the monument.

16   In honor of our nation's bicentennial in 1976, Great Britain presented a set of English "change ringing" bells to Congress. They are replicas of the bells in London's Westminster Abbey. Now known as the 'Congress Bells', they reside in a **tower**, which is managed by the NPS and was criticized in 1899 by the New York Times as, "looking like a cross between a cathedral and a cotton mill". Name the **tower**.

17   After the great Washington flood of 1881, Congress authorized the US Army Corps of Engineers to dredge and reclaim the land between the White House and the Potomac River. Besides creating land for the Lincoln and Jefferson Memorials, this

National Capital Region

reclamation project created more land for another NPS site. Name the additional site that benefited from the 1881 reclamation project.

18   Started as a garden hobby in 1882, these aquatic gardens have grown to 44 ponds with many species of water lilies, lotuses and wildlife. Name the gardens.

19   "O Captain! my Captain! Our fearful trip is done;
       The ship has weather'd every rack, the prize we sought is won;
       The port is near, the bells I hear, the people all exulting,
       While follow eyes the steady keel, the vessel grim and daring:
           But O heart! heart! heart!
               O the bleeding drops of red,
                   Where on the deck my Captain lies,
                       Fallen cold and dead."
       'O Captain! My Captain!', Walt Whitman

       President Abraham Lincoln was shot by John Wilkes Booth while watching a performance at this theatre. Name the theatre.

20   Congress ordered WWII support buildings to be knocked down to make way for these national gardens. What are they?

21   The names of more than 58,000 soldiers killed in war or missing in action are engraved in the black granite walls of this memorial, in the order they were lost. Name the memorial.

22   This 89-acre wooded island on the Potomac River, across from Georgetown, is a memorial to a great American outdoorsman, naturalist, hunter, scientist, politician and visionary. Stone plaques inscribed with his many famous quotations are surrounded by hiking trails leading through the island swamps, marshes and forest. Each year a military historic society conducts mock Civil War battles on the island. The island is home to many bird species, including the redheaded woodpecker and lesser scaup. Name the island.

23   "I have sworn upon the altar of
        God eternal hostility against
        every form of tyranny over
        the mind of man." . . . By recipient of this commemoration

        "We hold these truths to be self-evident:
        that all men are created equal,
        that they are endowed by their Creator
        with certain inalienable rights,
        among these are life, liberty and
        the pursuit of happiness."
                . . . Declaration of Independence

This memorial commemorates the author of the Declaration of
Independence and third U.S. president.It is popular in the
spring for its cherry blossoms. Name the memorial

24   The Japanese Government paid tribute to America by providing
        'A Gift of Trees' – hundreds of Japanese cherry trees. The trees
        were planted throughout the National Mall area and around this
        Basin. The NPS is guardian and caretaker of the trees. Each
        year the Smithsonian Institute conducts a National Cherry
        Blossom Festival, held the first two weeks of April, to celebrate
        the spectacular cherry blossoms. Year 2002 marked the 90th
        Anniversary of the Gift of Trees. Name the Basin the trees
        surround.

25   Soldiers in full battle gear, faces etched on a wall, and the
        words, "Freedom is not Free" are some of the highlights of this
        war memorial. Name the memorial.

26   This president honored Nobel Prize-winning authors,
        playwrights, doctors, and scientists at a White House state
        dinner. During his greeting remarks he said, "There hasn't been
        a collection of intelligence like this at the White House, except
        when Thomas Jefferson dined alone." What president made that
        remark?

National Capital Region

27   Abe Lincoln waited impatiently at the White House, pacing up and down, saying to those in earshot, "Damn . . . the Seventh Regiment is a myth . . . Why don't they come? Why don't they come? I don't believe there is any North!" Why?

28   What did President Franklin Delano Roosevelt request the National Geographic Society to donate to the White House during World War II?

29   During World War I, the U.S. Congress authorized a Bonus Expeditionary Force made up of volunteers. The volunteers were to receive a bonus when they finished their overseas tour of duty and returned to the States. Many returned and after waiting a year never received the promised bonus. Times were bad; people were poor, hungry and depressed. Hundreds of families marched on Washington and demanded their rightful bonus. They camped in tents for weeks on the National Mall. One day the president got bored with them and ordered the military to remove them. This army major was tasked with the removal. At night, this major led a tank division to the National Mall and demanded the squatters vacate. When they refused, shots rang out; and the tanks chased the BEF and their families across the Memorial Bridge into what is now Arlington Cemetery, Virginia. When the smoke cleared many men, women and children lay dead. What was the name of the Major?

30   "I am certain that after the dust of centuries has passed over cities, we, too, will be remembered not for victories or defeats in battle or politics, but for our contribution to the human spirit." Having said that, and in honor of his generous support of the performing arts, this great American is honored with a national performing arts center memorial in his name. Name the great American and the national center for the performing arts.

31   In 2000, Congress approved a new monument to be built in
      Washington, DC between the Washington and Lincoln
      Monuments to commemorate:
      A. Those Americans who served in World War II
      B. Women who served in Vietnam
      C. The handicapped of America
      D. None of the above

32   Battery Kemble, Fort Bayard, Fort Reno, Fort DeRussy, Fort
      Stevens, Fort Slocum, Fort Totten, and Fort Bunker Hill were
      some of the army posts used in the defense of what city? Hint:
      They formed a circle.

33   What fort bore the brunt of the only Confederate Army attack
      on Washington in July, 1864?

34   This NPS site once flourished, producing fine white flour,
      faster and less expensively than the competition. It outlived its
      time, and is now, more or less, a tranquil museum inside a D.C.
      park. Name this NPS site.

35   Congress authorized creation of this national historic site in
      1950 to exhibit its "great pre-Revolutionary architectural
      merit." In 1790, the town fathers banned free-running pigs and
      chickens in the streets in front of this historic site – the nerve of
      those fathers! The site is a remarkable heritage from our
      colonial period. Nestled today between shops in busy
      Georgetown, it once witnessed the loading and off-loading of
      cargo from sailing ships docked across the street on the
      Potomac River. Name this national historic site. Hint:Before
      congressional rescue, it served as a used car lot.

36   This NPS site was turned from an eye-sore into a scenic park
      with unprecedented recreational benefit. It now sports a nature
      center, planetarium, mill, visitor center, tennis courts,
      playgrounds, public golf course, boat house and hiking, biking
      and equestrian trails. Name this park.

National Capital Region

37   This site honors a great 19th-century African-American spokesman who fought to abolish slavery and for the civil rights of all oppressed people. Name the person this national historic site honors.

38   The National Council of Negro Women was founded at this national historic site by whom?

39   A certain Union general is given much credit for whipping the army into shape. In short order, it was well trained, well equipped and ready for action. But for months it did little more than train, drill, march and parade. This upset Abe Lincoln into remarking that, "If the general had no use for the army, he would like to borrow it." Who was the delinquent general?

CHAPTER 3 –
NATIONAL CAPITAL REGION
Answers

1   (George) Washington Monument.

2   For his skillful command of cavalry units. His son was Robert E. Lee.

3   White Georgia marble.

4   The number of states in the union at the time of Lincoln's death . . . their names are carved in the frieze directly above. The names of the 48 states in the union at the time the monument was completed in 1922 are carved in the exterior attic wall. A special plaque exists for Hawaii and Alaska.

5   Ulysses S. Grant Memorial.

6   They represent one room for each of FDR's presidential terms. He was the only president ever elected to four terms.

7   Correct answer is D.

8   The executive branch.

9   In 1814, the British burned the 'Executive Mansion' in retaliation for the destruction of some buildings in Canada by American forces. The exterior of the Executive Mansion was charred black and badly scarred. The architect ordered it to be whitewashed to hide the burn marks. It was then nicknamed the White House, and has been known by that name ever since. Formally known as the Executive Mansion, its name was not officially changed to the White House until 1901, by President Theodore Roosevelt.

10   The White House.

11   The White House.

12   George Washington.

13   The Tulip Library, of course. It is located between the Tidal Basin and the Washington Monument.

14   The Vietnam Veterans Memorial. A special statue of a nurse attending a wounded soldier in the midst of battle, sculptured by Glenna Goodacre, commemorates the women who served and sacrificed their lives in Vietnam.

15   U.S. Marine War Memorial – Albeit a national landmark, this monument is not part of the NPS.

16   Old Post Office Tower Pavilion, a unit of Pennsylvania Avenue National Historic Site.

17   The National Mall.
Sidebar – The National Mall is enjoyed by millions of visitors each year who come to view the nation's spectacular fire-works display, listen to outdoor concerts and political speeches, picnic and fly kites, play softball, throw Frisbees, or attend the annual Smithsonian Folklife Festival.

18   Kenilworth Park and Aquatic Gardens.

19   Ford's Theatre NHS.

20   Constitution Gardens on the National Mall; collectors can obtain a Passport cancellation at National Mall, 900 Ohio Dr, WDC

21   Vietnam Veterans Memorial on the National Mall.

22   Theodore Roosevelt Island.

23   Thomas Jefferson Memorial.

24   Tidal Basin, Thomas Jefferson Memorial.
Sidebar – Over the past 50 years, on average, the cherry blossoms peaked on April 8th. It should be seen by all Americans at least once in a lifetime.

25   Korean War Veterans Memorial.

26   John F. Kennedy, 35th US President.

27   The Confederates were invading Washington and laying siege to the city . . . Lincoln was afraid he would have to surrender. The Northern army was three days overdue. Needless-to-say, the army arrived and drove the Confederates out of Washington.

28   Roosevelt asked for a set of the Geographic's fine maps of Europe, Asia, and the Pacific. The Geographic was quick to respond, and provided Roosevelt with a full set of all of their maps, enclosed in a beautiful, wall-mount, oak wood cabinet. Individual maps can be selected and easily slid-out on trays. Roosevelt had the map case built into the wall of the Oval Office, where it still sees use today.

29   Major Dwight D. Eisenhower, 34th US President . . . Now you know the rest of the story.

30   John F. Kennedy, 35th US President; The John F. Kennedy Center for the Performing Arts, WDC.

31   Correct answer is A.

32   Civil War defenses of Washington; Fort Circle Parks, WDC.

33   Fort Stevens; Fort Circle Parks, WDC.

34   Pierce Mill, a unit of Rock Creek Park, WDC.

35   Old Stone House, WDC.

National Capital Region

36   Rock Creek Park, WDC.

37   Frederick Douglas NHS, WDC.

38   Mary McLeod Bethune NHS, WDC.

39   Major General George B. McClellan, who was later removed from the job of general in chief.

CHAPTER 4 -
PACIFIC NORTHWEST AND ALASKA REGION
Questions and Answers

Pacific Northwest and Alaska Region consists of four states – Alaska, Washington, Idaho and Oregon – and embodies the majority of land under the care of the National Park Service.

Pacific Northwest and Alaska Region

For a complete list of park sites to visit in this Region go to Appendix A.

CHAPTER 4 -
PACIFIC NORTHWEST AND ALASKA REGION
Questions

1   Wrangell-St. Elias National Park gets its name from two mighty mountains within its borders – Mount Wrangell and Mount St. Elias. How did Mount St. Elias get its name?
    A. Like hurricanes, mountains are sometimes named after saints and Elias was next in line.
    B. St. Elias is the patron saint of the National Park Service.
    C. Saint Elias was born on this mountain.
    D. Russian explorers discovered this mountain on St. Elias day.

2   The Valley of the 10,000 Smokes can be enjoyed at what national park?

3   Visitors can sit at a sidewalk café, enjoy the haggling of buying and selling fish at Pikes Market, watch the ferries cross the sound, and view a snow-capped national park in the distance. Name the snow-capped national park.

4   This national park is rebounding – growing in elevation – approximately $1\frac{1}{2}$ inches per year. What national park would that be?

5   I am a western tiger swallowtail and I frequent the lowlands on both sides of the mountains at North Cascades National Park. What am I?

6   Heralded as, "The last grand adventure of its kind that the world will ever know," this adventure is commemorated at what national historical park?

7   Notorious criminal "Soapy" Smith, a con-man and a bully, reigned by terror at this Alaskan frontier site. Eventually, he was shot dead in a gun battle with John Reid, leader of a vigilante group. Reid died twelve days later. Both men are buried together at this NHS. Name the town and NHS.

8   "Those who contemplate the beauty of the earth find reserves of strength that will endure as long as life lasts." Rachel Carson.

Alaska set aside a 48,000-acre preserve especially for this magnificent bird. What bird is so honored, and what is the name of the preserve?

9   "If this rain of death has produced so disastrous an effect on birds, what of other lives, including our own?" . . . . "The Sedge is wither'd from the lake, And no birds sing." Silent Spring, *Guess*

Through her relentless 10-year attack against the chemical industry's use of DDT as a pesticide, this talented and patient lady saved the bald eagle and peregrine falcon from certain extinction. She successfully proved that DDT was softening eagle and peregrine egg-shells and, consequently, preventing new clutches from hatching. Who was this incredible marine biologist from Maine?

10   Headlines screamed "Gold, Gold, Gold," which launched thousands to stampede to the Yukon gold fields to strike it rich in 1897 and 1898. Jack London was among them. They fought against time, each other, severe weather and the mysterious northern wilderness. London documented the suffering of man and animal, and the mysteries of the wilderness, in his many novels and short stories, e.g., To Build A Fire, Call of the Wild, White Fang and Sea Wolf. There were two ways to get to the gold fields; by an all- water route up the Yukon River, or by land and a shorter raft trip floating down the Yukon River. To get to the Yukon River by land, however, was no picnic, for stampeders had to cross a treacherous mountain pass. Canadian North West Mounted Police required each person entering the

Pacific Northwest and Alaska Region

Canadian Yukon to bring 2,000 pounds of provisions – a year's supply. Many waited on long lines for a turn to carry this burden on their back, struggling to make numerous trips over and back. The top gets 200 inches of snow and temperatures as low as -50°F. John Muir wrote of the pass, "It looked like an anthill someone stirred with a stick." What is the name of the mountain pass and who is it named after?

11   A moose attempted to swim across a fjord at Glacier Bay NP when it was attacked and eaten by a few of these mammals. Name the mammal.

12   Glacier Bay National Park is flanked by a magnificent mountain range with a very misleading name. Name the mountain range. Hint: John Muir once described Glacier Bay as, "Dark, damp, dismal and mysterious."

13   I am a wild coast with extraordinary features – fjords, glaciers, ice-flows, forested mountains, Harding ice-field, seabirds and sea mammals. I offer fun outdoor adventures galore – sailing, sight-seeing, mountain climbing, cruising, ice-field hiking, glacier and wildlife viewing, and ranger-led tours. What am I?

14   Name the three bear species found in Alaska.

15   What is a hawk's favorite dessert?

16   Alaskans have a nickname for the first snowfall of the season; that light snow that covers the slopes and turns the leaves. What is its nickname?

17   The glacier at the end of Kenai Fjord is known as _____ Glacier. Name the Glacier. It is predominately what color?

18   In 1836, Marcus and Narcissa Whitman and fellow missionaries founded a Protestant mission near Walla Walla, Washington to convert Cayuse Indians to Christianity. They also set up a way-station for Oregon Trail pioneers. A measles epidemic killed half of the Cayuse people. They blamed the

epidemic on the missionaries. How did the Cayuse avenge the measles victims?

19   Forever-shifting, wind-blown dunes, hundreds of feet high, line the shores of this national recreation area. In a few places, dunes have migrated six miles inland, rolling over trees, vegetation and roadways. Mountain streams have been dammed by sand and lakes formed; lakes have filled with sand and dried up. As trees are semi-buried in sand, they are starved for moisture and nutrients, and soon die. Blasted over decades by windstorms of sand and salt water, desolate trees become bleached-gray, barren and mysterious. These arcane skeletons are known by a nickname. Name the secret trees' nickname and the national recreation area.

20   One of the NPS' newest national monuments, this volcanic land of lava is a fun place. For a great adventure, drive to the top of Lava Butte (only for the brave – narrow, one-lane, twisting road to the summit at 5,020-ft), and take a short $\frac{1}{4}$ –mile hike around crater rim on Cinder Trail with a park ranger. What a great view of the surrounding Cascade Mountains and a look into the 180-ft deep crater! If you're still bored and have some energy stored, hike Trail of the Whispering Pines or Trail of the Molten Lava. Both offer a great photo-opp. Name the new park.

21   "Ever thicker, thicker, thicker,
            Froze the ice on lake and river,
            Ever deeper, deeper, deeper;
            Fell the snow o'er all the landscape."
                One of Ours, Willa Cather, Pulitzer Prize, 1922.

Although Willa never made it to this national park, her poem describes it eloquently. The last time the author was at this NP, only the tops of Douglas fir were visible in the parking lot. NPS staff continuously plowed and shoveled, plowed and shoveled, to create a path to the visitor center. Snow formed a tunnel, head and shoulders high, at the visitor center entrance, and at select viewing stations overlooking a great lake. The lake is the center of attraction at an elevation of 6,176-feet and a depth of 1,932-feet, with the bluest of blue waters.

Accommodations at the park lodge are exquisite . . . no phones, no TV, just peace and quiet, rest and relaxation, fine dining and a walk-in stone fire-place where whole logs are burned. Dine while watching the sun slip behind the caldera rim. What is this fabulous national park?

22   Where is Phantom Ship located? Hint: At the deepest lake in America.

23   "At this place we . . . wintered and remained
      from the 7th Decr.1805 to this day
      and have lived as well as we had the right to expect . . ."
            William Clark, March 23, 1806.

In 1805-06, the Lewis and Clark expedition wintered at this national memorial site. Name the site.

24   In 1909, this president established Mount Olympus National Monument (later to become Olympic National Park) to protect the peninsula's elk. The elk were then named in his honor. Name the president.

25   This national park set a record when it received 1,122-inches of snowfall in the winter of 1971-72. Name the park.

26   Wizard Island is found at what national park?

27   Conservationists argued against construction of the Alaskan pipeline, from Prudhoe Bay to Valdez, because they believed heavy tanker traffic in Prince William Sound would result in an eventual oil spill. While Congress was preparing to vote for or against the pipeline, this US president was "taped" saying, "Not to worry, an oil spill will never happen" . . . of course, it did happen. What US president made that remark?

28   In 1874, Elijah Davidson followed a bear into a cave and found, not a bear, but an extraordinary marble cave system. Inside the cave he found pillars, columns and curtains of stone and massive rooms as grand as any modern day cathedral. Above ground he found meadows of delicate wildflowers, in every color of the rainbow, and old-growth forests. What national monument did Elijah discover?

29   Monkeys that eat potato chips can be found at Oregon Caves National Monument. What are the monkeys called?

30   At cave sites, the NPS installed security gates to keep people out during off-hours. The gates are made of bars that are positioned horizontally and spaced to convenience this mammal's passage. Name the mammal.

31   "Big Tree" is a madrone that is over 200 feet high and about 12 feet in diameter. At what national monument can it be found?

32   This amphibian barks when in danger. Name the amphibian and the NPS NM where it is most likely to be seen.

33   This endangered owl will only live in old growth forests; it is especially fond of Oregon Caves National Monument. Name the owl.

34   This gentleman worked for the Hudson Bay Company, directing the fur trade at Fort Vancouver. His transactions with the Indians, key players in the fur trade industry, kept the peace and earned him great respect. His home, across the Columbia River from Fort Vancouver, was twice moved and is now a national historic site. Name the NHS.

35   The NPS has researched back 20 million years to highlight and enhance the natural value of this national monument for its visitors. Remnants of prior arcane eras are evidenced throughout the park. A unique treasure, once concealed, is now exposed in the sedimentary rock for visitors to enjoy. Name the national monument.

36   What two puffin species can be found in Alaskan national parks?

37   'Island in Time Trail' and 'Painted Cove Trail' are excellent hikes that are found at what national monument?

38   At Ebey's Landing National Historic Reserve, Washington, 19th-century settlers claimed land for homesteading under what land act?

39   This large bird is a common all-year visitor to Crater Lake NP and likes to hang out at the caldera rim, near the gift shop and snack bar. (Don't feed them!) It is one of the few birds in the world to cache food for winter. Name the bird.

40   "Alaska is not, as the license plates assert, the 'Last Frontier'. Alaska is the final big bite on the American table, where there is never enough to go around . . . for Americans Alaska is the last pork chop." What famous American naturalist and author made that remark after visiting Alaska in 1982?

41   When asked why he granted permission to chase and hunt this animal by helicopter, Governor Hickel of Alaska replied, "You just can't let nature run wild." Unbelievable and wild (pun intended) as his statement may seem, what animal did Governor Hickel allowed to be aerial-hunted?

42   Activity is plentiful at this national historical park. Hike to the top of Mount Finlayson, where on a clear day you can see breath-taking views in all directions; Mt. Baker to the east, Mt. Rainier to the southeast, the Olympic Mountains to the south, and British Columbian Range to the west. Walk the beaches, at low tide observe the tidal pools, spy on shore birds – terns, gulls, plovers, turnstones, greater and lesser yellowlegs, hawks and a pair of bald eagles nesting at the visitor center – survey the ocean for bay or sea ducks, cormorants, and an occasional falcon or osprey, and whale-watch. Enjoy the solitude of the Douglas fir forest, pay close attention, you may spot a deer or two. Name this national historical park. Hint: Visit the harbor on Friday . . . Fourth of July here is more than a holiday.

43   Between 1859 and 1872, the United States Army and Great
      Britain's Royal Marines stood face-to-face in armed readiness
      for war, in what became known as the "Pig War" confrontation.
      Both militaries remained on this island for 13 years, ready to
      go to war at a moment's notice, until the ownership of the
      island was decided by Germany's Kaiser Wilhelm I. It is now a
      national historical park – name it.

44   List Alaska's 'Big 8'. Hint: It has nothing to do with college
      football.

45   Found at Katmai NP, Denali NP, Wrangell - St. Elias NP and
      several other parks, this mammal is North America's largest
      rodent. Name the animal.

46   How well do you know Alaska's beavers? Answer true or false:
      A. Beaver eat the bark of trees and cambium layer just
          beneath the bark, but never the wood. _____
      B. Beaver can hold their breath underwater for 30-
          minutes._____
      C. In winter, Beaver breathe air bubbles trapped beneath
          the ice. _____
      D. Beaver new-born are called cubs. _____
      E. Beaver cache food for winter by jabbing sticks and
          branches into the mud at the bottom of their pond.

          _____

47   How well do you know Alaska's arctic fox? Answer true or
      false:
      A. Arctic foxes frequently follow polar bear around,
          because the bears eat only seal blubber and leave
          behind a feast of meat for the fox. _____
      B. Arctic foxes are known to criss-cross winter pack ice
          in traveling across the Bering Strait to Russia.

          _____
      C. Arctic foxes tunnel into a washed-up whale carcass
          until it resembles a piece of Swiss cheese _____
      D. Arctic foxes have no known predators. _____
      E. Where arctic and red fox territories overlap, red fox
          will dig up arctic fox dens and kill them. _____

48   The body temperature of this chirpy fellow falls below freezing while hibernating. Every few weeks it wakes up, warms up, leaves the den, eliminates waste, and returns to hibernation. It can be found at Gates of the Arctic National Park and Preserve. Name the animal.

49   Snowy owl, snowshoe hare, arctic fox, short-tailed weasel, and willow, rock and white-tailed ptarmigan are Alaskan wildlife that share something in common. What is it?

50   Several species of whales are regularly seen at Glacier Bay NP, Cape Krusenstern NM, Bering Land Bridge National Preserve, Kenai Fjords NP, Sitka NHP and Arctic National Wildlife Refuge. Name three whales that can be spotted off the coast of Alaska's national parks.

51   Scientists believe it is across this national preserve that the first humans crossed over from Asia to North America. Name the national preserve.

52   Where did the brown bear get its nickname "Grizzly Bear"?

53   Living above the timberline in the tundra of Brooks Range, these mammals dig a network of connected underground dens near boulder fields or rock slides. Expect to find them at Noatak National Preserve and Gates of the Arctic National Park and Preserve, as well as in most mountainous areas of Alaska. Name the mammal.

54   Balls of cotton grow at the tip of each plant. It grows straight and tall and green, filling valleys at Arctic National Wildlife Refuge. In the summer, whole fields take on the appearance of a green sea with white polka-dots. Name the plant.

55   Name three wild berries important to brown- and black-bear diets.

56   This mammal reverses its hind feet to climb head-first down
      trees, leaps nine feet horizontally between trees, and can jump
      20 feet to the ground, without injury. Its curiosity causes it to
      examine every hollow tree it encounters, making it an easy
      target to trap. It is reported that one researcher trapped the same
      individual 77 times. Name this mammal, which makes its home
      in Denali NP.

57   Winter in Alaska brings the gravest threat to mountain goats
      and Dall sheep. They are more likely to die in winter than any
      other time of year; excluding predators, they commonly die
      from starvation caused by inability to free ice-covered grasses,
      falls from slippery slopes, hyperthermia freezing immature and
      aged ones, and _____. Name the fourth greatest
      winter killer of goats and sheep.

58   This mammal is the only member of the deer family in which
      both sexes grow antlers. Its 5-inch hooves make good paddles,
      snowshoes for crossing deep snow, and shovels for digging
      through snow to find food. Name the deer, which is plentiful at
      Kobuk Valley NP, Denali NP, Gateway to the Arctic NP and
      Pres., and Arctic National Wildlife Refuge and Pres.

59   This mammal has acquired the handle 'Nomad of the North'.
      Name the mammal.

60   Name the national park that is 26 miles north of the Arctic
      Circle.

61   Five species of salmon can be fished from a wild river at this
      NPS site. Name the site and three of the salmon species.

Pacific Northwest and
Alaska Region

62   This ice-age leftover once bunked with the epic mammoth
        elephant and woolly rhinoceros. Like the extinct mammoth and
        rhinoceros, the last Alaskan species of this massive animal was
        hunted to its death in 1865. In 1930, the U.S. Department of the
        Interior purchased 34 from Greenland and reintroduced them to
        Alaska. Today, they can be spotted over most of their original
        Alaska range. Their stronghold, however, is at Nunivak Island.
        The Inupiat Eskimos' nickname for this impressive animal is
        the "bearded one". Name this animal.

63   At this national preserve the Inupiat Eskimos herd reindeer,
        which were imported to Alaska from Europe as a domestic
        meat source. Migratory birds from all seven continents find
        nesting habitat here. Hot springs with water temperaturess of
        134°F degrees can be sampled here. Name the national
        preserve (N PRES).

64   Upright whale ribs, a common sight at northern Alaska
        preserves, are a traditional Eskimo symbol for what?

65   If "the Earth laughs in flowers", as Ralph Waldo Emerson said,
        then this NPS region giggles all spring, summer and fall. Name
        any four wild-flowers from the NPS Pacific Alaska Region.

66   Purple Kamchatka – rare at Bering Land Bridge N PRES, but
        common in Siberia – are a beautiful flower that blooms on
        what plant?

67   A Russian czar hired a Danish explorer and sent him to
        determine if Asia were connected to North America. This took
        place in 1741. Name the czar, the Danish explorer and what it
        was that he discovered.

68   This mammal can be found at most parks in the NPS Pacific
        Alaska Region. It is principally a vegetarian with a low-salt
        diet. For this reason, it acquired the nasty habit of stealing
        sweaty hiker boots and backpacks, from which it sucks the
        salty sweat. It also enjoys the inner, cambium layer of the bark
        of trees. Name the mammal.

69   The female of this species is called a vixen. It is commonly seen from the tour bus at Denali NP. Name the animal.

70   Identify which of the below Alaska wildlife statements are true or false:

A.   When called by hunters, by blowing on a blade of grass like a whistle, Sitka black-tailed deer seek out the hunter. _____

B.   If grasped in the talons of a raptor, a weasel squirms and twists, until it is in position to bite the raptor in the neck, killing it _____

C.   Snowshoe hare dig complex tunnels and elaborate dens that they line with big game fur. _____

D.   Gymnasts – snowshoe hare leap and twist in midair, stand on hind their legs and box each other with forepaws. _____

E.   A short-tailed weasel can drag prey weighing ten times its own body weight to its den. _____

F   Beluga whales talk to each other through a series of shrieks, whistles and birdlike calls. _____

G   Beluga whales do not feed in fresh water. _____

H   Beluga whales shed their skin each summer.
      _____

I   Bouncing sound waves off objects is a navigation method some marine mammals use, called shirkology. _____

J   Eskimos and other Native Americans still harpoon whale and shoot caribou at America's national park preserves. _____

K   Polar bear paws are covered with fur to muffle sound so they can sneak up on prey. _____

71   Pound-for-pound, this animal is the most feared in its ecosystem. It is known as the "hyena of the north". Its scientific name means "glutton". Name the animal found in most Alaskan NPs.

Pacific Northwest and Alaska Region

72   This marine mammal is often seen off the coast of Cape Krusenstern NM and Bering Land Bridge NP RES, but resides mostly at Round Island. It uses a rock for a pillow. Name the mammal. Hint: It has been known to bite a grizzly bear to death.

73   This great whale was nearly hunted to extinction, but due to the efforts of Greenpeace, the Sierra Club, NPS, the Audubon Society, and many other save-the-whales programs, this species has recovered, and has since been removed from the endangered-species list. It summers off Alaska's coast and can be seen from Sitka NHP, Cape Krusenstern NM, and Bering Land Bridge NP RES, among others. It winters at its breeding grounds along Mexico's Baja California coast.Its migration is the longest of any migrating marine mammal. Name this phenomenal, unpretentious animal.

74   This year-round resident of the Bering Land Bridge NP RES can open its mouth wide enough to swallow a full-grown polar bear. Name the marine mammal.

75   These marine mammals, the fastest in the sea, often catch and pass the NPS- sponsored cruise ship – Spirit of Adventure – as it tours the fjords of Glacier Bay NP. Name the marine mammal.

76   Diving sea ducks in large flocks are scarce in the lower 48 States, but this duck is plentiful along the fjord coasts of Glacier Bay NP. Name this bird. Hint: It is black with several white patches and a cinnamon belly.

77   Known to flip harbor seals high into the air, playing with them as a cat toys with a mouse, before eating them, this mammal sometimes kills moose as they swim across the icy Strait of Glacier Bay NP. Name the mammal. Hint: It is known as the wolf of the sea.

78   This gregarious marine mammal sleeps on the open sea. It often holds hands with a mate or chum so that they don't drift apart while they sleep. For the same reason, when close to shore it will wrap itself in the kelp growing on the ocean bottom. Name the sociable mammal.

79   In 1741, naturalist Georg Wilhelm Steller accompanied Vitus Bering on his trek to Alaska and discovered this marine mammal, which now bears his name. He described this mammal as having a shaggy mane, long whiskers and a roar like a lion. Name the marine mammal.

80   This marine mammal has a set of air sacs that it can inflate to the size of a basketball to help keep it afloat while it sleeps on the open sea. Name the marine mammal.

81   What's the size of an elephant, but doesn't weigh anything?

82   Looking like a guinea pig and sounding like a squeaky rubber toy, this tiny ball of fur lives in the rocky slopes of Mount McKinley, Denali NP and the Alaskan Range, Wrangell – St. Elias NP. Name the tiny mammal.

83   Totem poles, 1804 battlefield, fort and the Russian Bishop's House are some of the attractions at this national historical park. Who fought who in 1804 and what is the name of this NHP? Hint: Established in 1910, it's the oldest and smallest national park in Alaska.

84   Volcano inside volcano, volcanic landscape with one of the world's largest calderas are the high points of this national monument and preserve. Name the park.

85   Name the original occupants of Glacier Bay.

Pacific Northwest and Alaska Region

86   Home to two active volcanoes, Dena'ina Indians lived here for eons, Dall sheep graze its alpine meadows, caribou herds travel through, and backpacking, fishing and river running are fun things humans like to do at this national park and preserve. Name this peaceful national park. Hint: The Alaskan and Aleutian Ranges join here at the Chigmit Mountains.

87   Summering at Kenai Fjords NP, it heads to South America for the winter; traveling 25,000 miles roundtrip – the longest journey of any animal. Name this ambitious, tireless traveler.

88   This central Alaska national preserve saw lots of activity during the 1898 gold rush era. Name the national preserve.

89   A stockade, blacksmith shop, bake-house, wash-house, kitchen quarters, fur warehouse, bastion, carpenter shop, Chief Factor's house, farm and orchard are all an integral part of this national historic site. Name the site. Hint: It fired greetings to Columbia ships.

90   What is the name of the unassuming, yet dignified, chief, leader, peacemaker, and skilled diplomat of the Nez Perce during their epic flight from the army? Hint: He was born in a cave near Nez Perce NHP, Idaho.

91   Inupiat Heritage Center Barrows, Alaska honors the contribution Inupiat Eskimo people made to the success of what adventurous 18th – 19th century industry?

92   A moon-like landscape comes to life as you explore Indian Tunnel lava tube or Inferno Cone at this national monument. Name the national monument.

93   Popular access to North Cascades National Park, which is
      nearly all wildernesses, is via three adjoining waterways.
      Which waterway is not affiliated with North Cascades National
      Park?
      A.   Ross Lake NRA
      B.   Olympic Lake NRA
      C.   Lake Roosevelt NRA
      D.   Lake Chelan NRA

94   Named after massive granite rock formations, this national
      reserve is 2.5 billion years old. Name the national reserve. Hint:
      It reminded passing pilgrims of city buildings.

95   The largest collection of fossil horses in North America can be
      seen at what national monument?

Pacific Northwest and
Alaska Region

CHAPTER 4 -
PACIFIC NORTHWEST AND ALASKA REGION
Answers

1   Correct answer is D.

2   Katmai NP, Alaska.

3   Mt Olympic NP.
     Sidebar-If you stay in Seattle, do yourself a favor and check out the 'Underground', and stay at the 'Pioneer Square Hotel'.

4   Glacier Bay NP, Alaska.

5   A beautiful yellow, with tiger-like black stripes, butterfly.

6   Klondike Gold Rush NHP, Skagway, Alaska.

7   Skagway, now part of Klondike Gold Rush NHP, Alaska.

8   The bald eagle; the Alaska Chilkat Bald Eagle Preserve.

9   Rachel Carson.

10   Chilkoot Pass is named after the local Chilkoot Indian tribe; once known exclusively as Canada's Chilkoot Trail NHS, it joined the Thirty Mile Heritage River (Yukon River), Dawson Historic Complex NHS and United States Seattle, Skagway, Chilkoot and White Pass NPS units to become part of Klondike Gold Rush International Historical Park.

11   Orca "killer" whale; visitors to Glacier Bay NP are almost assured of seeing a whale – most likely a humpback or orca. Sidebar – For a small daily fee (about $12) the NPS will provide two-person kayaks with paddles, boots, skirt protection and lessons. To avoid happening to guests what happened to the

moose, park rangers prohibit kayakers from crossing fjords. Instead, to get to the other side of fjord, kayakers must paddle close to the shore and take the long way around.

12   Fairweather Range – an unlikely name since the mountains are socked-in by clouds most of the year.

13   Kenai Fjords NP, Seward, Alaska.

14   Black bear, brown bear (grizzly) and polar bear.

15   A chocolate milk-snake . . . had to throw in some humor.

16   Termination dust.

17   Exit Glacier, Kenai Fjords NP; its color is ice blue.

18   Cayuse executed Marcus Whitman, his wife and 11 pioneers . . . they held 50 others hostage. The hostages were ransomed by the Hudson Bay Company.

19   'Ghost Trees'; Oregon Dunes NRA, Gold Beach, Oregon. Sidebar – Nearby the NRA, the State of Oregon maintains a viewing area where you are certain to see a herd of Roosevelt elk.

20   Newberry National Volcanic Monument, Bend, Oregon.

21   Crater Lake NP, Oregon.
Sidebar – For a great vacation, stay at Crater Lake Lodge . . . best seat in the house . . . originally build in 1903, it has been refurbished, but still maintains its rustic, timber-design warmth. For information call (541) 830-8700, e-mail: info@crater-lake.com or try the web at www.crater-lake.com.

22   Crater Lake NP, Oregon.

23   Fort Clatsop N MEM, Oregon.

24   Teddy Roosevelt, 26th US President; the elk were officially
named Roosevelt elk.

25   Mount Rainier NP, Washington.

26   Crater Lake NP, Oregon.
Sidebar – The NPS takes visitors over to Wizard Island a few
times a day in a small boat. The hike from the caldera rim to
the lake and back, however, is strenuous.

27   Richard Nixon, 37th US President.

28   Oregon Caves NM, Cave Junction, OR.
Sidebar – Oregon Caves NM is so much more than a cave. It is
a warm, inspiring place with spectacular views of the
surrounding mountains and valleys. Hiking through the old-
growth forests is a reward in itself, for you are sure to see
wildlife, e.g., Steller's jays, deer, flying squirrel and
chipmunks. For a charming evening, stay at the park's 1930s
vintage lodge, the Chateau. Oregon Caves Company, a private
concessionaire, conducts daily tours through the cave. The half-
mile tour takes about 75 minutes, with 500 stairs that are
sometimes steep and wet. Hence, the tour is not for everyone,
especially if you have walking, breathing or heart problems . . .
like me.

29   Chip Monks . . . ha, ha!

30   Bats . . . specifically, Townsend's big-eared bats and pallid bats
at Oregon Caves NM . . . Horizontal bars, rather than vertical
bars, allow bat wings to maneuver through the gate.

31   Oregon Caves NM, Cave Junction, OR.

32   Pacific giant salamander – rust colored with black spots;
Oregon Caves NM, Cave Junction, OR.

33   Spotted Owl.

34   McLoughlin House NHS, Portland, Oregon.

35   John Day Fossil Beds NM, Oregon.

36   The horned and tufted puffins can be found only in the waters
      off Alaska.

37   John Day Fossil Beds NM, Oregon.
      Sidebar – Along 'Island in Time Trail' NPS paleontologists
      exposed arcane fossils of saber-tooth tigers, prehistoric
      elephants, miniature horses, camels, rhinos and other animals
      no longer found in North America. The NPS has done a nice
      job protecting them, where they were found, in glass cases to
      prevent damage from the elements. Along 'Painted Cove Trail'
      expect to see painted hills, hundreds of feet high, in vividly-
      hued sand layers of red, pink, green, bronze, tan and black. At
      dusk, we saw a herd of 30 mule deer.

38   Donation Land Claim Act.

39   Clark's nutcracker.

40   Edward Abbey

41   The threatened gray wolf.

42   San Juan Island NHP, Washington.
      Sidebar – Washington State Ferry service is available from
      Anacortes, 83 miles north of Seattle, to Friday Harbor. Call
      (360) 378-5240 for more information. Fourth (4th) of July is
      the name of a beach at the park.

43   San Juan Island NHP, Washington.
      Sidebar – San Juan Island is one of many in a cluster. Put your
      car or RV on the ferry at Anacortes, WA, and enjoy a beautiful
      cruise through the narrow passages. A hot breakfast or lunch is
      available on the ferry. Charming marine villages and small,
      quaint fishing boats can be enjoyed to and fro.

44   The following big-game mammals can be found together only in Alaska: caribou, Dall sheep, mountain goat, brown/grizzly bear, walrus, musk ox, gray wolf, and polar bear.

45   Beaver.

46   Correct answers: A = True; B = False, 15 minutes; C = True; D = False, Kits; E = True.

47   Correct answers: A = True; B = True; C = True; D = False, predators are wolves, polar bears, golden eagles, snowy owls and humans; E = True.

48   Arctic ground squirrel.

49   They are white in winter.

50   Beluga, bowhead, gray, humpback, minke and killer whales – also known as orcas.

51   Bering Land Bridge National Preserve, Nome, Alaska.

52   From its hoary, grisly, grizzled fur.

53   Three species of marmot, with hoary marmot the most common.

54   Cotton-grass.

55   Crowberry, cranberry, blueberry, blackberry, strawberry and raspberry.

56   Marten.

57   Avalanches.

58   Caribou.

59   Caribou.

60   Kobuk Valley NP, Kotzebue, AK.

61   Alagnak Wild River, King Salmon, Alaska; king, chum, chinook, sockeye (or red) and silver salmon.

62   Musk ox.

63   Bering Land Bridge NP RES

64   Eskimo burial place.

65   Lupine, fireweed, arctic poppies, pink plumes, the many berries, yellow and red Indian paintbrush, dwarf dogwood, cinquefoil, purslane, cottongrass, red Columbine, Siberian aster, false lily-of-the-valley, Scammon spring beauty, skunk cabbage, saxifrage, pasqueflower, forget-me-nots, white yarrow, squirreltail, dryas, dwarf monkey, sky pilot, monkshood, yellow monkey, pink mountain heather, glacier lilies, rabbit-brush, pinedrops, knotweed, phlox, aster fleabone, spires, western anemone, dirty socks and sulphur eriogonum, to name a few of the favorites.

66   Rhododendron.

67   Peter the Great; Vitus Bering; Vitus was the first European to set eyes on Alaska and he, so-called, discovered Alaska. Sidebar - The Bering Straits and, consequently, Bering Land Bridge NP RES are named after him.

68   Porcupine.

69   Red fox.

70   Correct answers are: A = True; B = True; C = False, they live on the surface under brush; D = True; E = True; F = True; G = False; they swim hundreds of miles up- river to feed on spawning salmon; H = True; I = False; it is known as echo-location. J = True; K = True.

71   Wolverine.

72   Walrus.
      Sidebar – Walrus range from 2000 to 4000 pounds, while the
      largest grizzly weighs in at about 1500 pounds. Once in the
      water, walrus can easily outmaneuver grizzly. Acting in self-
      defense, walrus have been known to grasp a grizzly and sink its
      39-inch tusks – extended canine teeth – into the grizzly's neck,
      killing it. Polar bears kill and eat walrus calves.

73   Gray whale.

74   Bowhead whale.

75   Dall porpoise.
      Sidebar – The daily cruise to the glaciers is led by a park
      ranger who is a knowledgeable naturalist and interpreter. The
      cruise is as educational as it is relaxing and enjoyable . . .
      praise, credits and kudos to the NPS! They keep the fjords
      quiet, as well as protecting and preserving it for the future.
      Spirit of Adventure is owned and operated by private
      concessionaires; call 1-800-451-5952 for reservations and
      information.

76   Harlequin duck.

77   Killer whale – orcas.

78   Sea otter

79   Steller sea lion.

80   Walrus.

81   An elephant's shadow.

82   Pika.

83   The Russians fought Native American Tlingits for control of
       Alaska; Sitka NHP, Sitka, Alaska.
       Sidebar – The Tlingits are gregarious people whose totem-pole
       collection at Sitka is, in my opinion, the finest in the world.

84   Aniakchak NM PRES, Alaska Peninsula.

85   Tlingit Indians.

86   Lake Clark NP PRES, Alaska.

87   Arctic tern.

88   Yukon-Charley Rivers N PRES, Eagle, Alaska.

89   Fort Vancouver NHS, Washington.

90   Chief Joseph.

91   Whaling.
       Sidebar - Inupiat Heritage Center is an affiliate of New Bedford
       Whaling NHP, Massachusetts.

92   Craters of the Moon NM, Idaho.

93   Correct answer is B.

94   City of Rocks N RES, Burley, Idaho.

95   Hagerman Fossil Beds NM, Idaho.

CHAPTER 5 –
WESTERN, HAWAII, GUAM AND
AMERICAN SAMOA REGION
Questions and Answers

Western Region includes California, Arizona, Nevada, Hawaii, Guam and American Samoa.

Western, Hawaii, Guam and American Samoa Region

HAWAII

1935
BOULDER DAM

Originally named Hoover, changed to Boulder and now Hoover again, this great structure is one of the world's largest dams.

MARINES

JOHN MUIR

(1838-1914) Naturalist instrumental in founding of U.S. National Parks.

One little known fact about California is the oldest living trees on earth are some bristlecone pines 4500 years old in the Inyo National Forest.

For a complete list of park sites to visit in this Region go to Appendix A.

CHAPTER 5 –
WESTERN, HAWAII, GUAM AND
AMERICAN SAMOA REGION
Questions

1   Portuguese explorer Joao Rodriguez Cabrilho was the first European to sight this chain of islands, which later became a national park. Name the islands.

2   Sometime in the late 1980's a volcano at this national park began oozing oodles of lava into the Pacific Ocean, and continues to do so today. Name the national park and the volcano.

3   "I think that I shall never see,
A poem as lovely as a tree.

A tree whose hungry mouth is pressed,
Against the earth's sweet flowing breast.

A tree that looks at God all day,
And lifts her leafy arms to pray.

A tree that may in summer wear,
A nest of robins in her hair.

Upon whose bosom snow has lain,
Who intimately lives with rain.

Poems are made by fools like me,
But only God can make a tree."
                    Trees
                    By: Joyce Kilmer

Three national parks in California, known for their majestic trees, best personify this poem. Name the three parks. (May trees be always with you!)

4   This NPS site is the home of the only American to win the Nobel Prize for Literature in the drama category. He also won the Pulitzer Prize four times. Name the author and the national park historic site.

5   This talented conservationist stood atop the Sierra Nevada and said:
>   "Climb the mountains and get their good tidings.
>   Nature's peace will flow into you as sunshine flows into trees.
>   The winds will blow their own freshness into you,
>   Storms their energy, while cares will drop off like autumn leaves."

What great American conservationist said these inspiring words?

6   Who is buried at Eugene O'Neill's Tao House?

7   In 1915 this mountain peak burst into eruption, sending an enormous mushroom cloud seven miles into the atmosphere. The eruption lasted on-and-off for seven years.Today, the mountain receives so much snow that this national park is closed to vehicle traffic from September through May. Park rangers, however, conduct a free, ranger-led, snowshoe hike every Saturday. The NPS provides snowshoes for a donation of $1, and expert lessons. The snowshoe hike to the bubbling thermal hot springs is a great way to spend a day outdoors in the winter. Name the mountain and national park.

8   The Disney Corporation and the Sierra Club fought a lengthy legal battle over Disney's proposed ski resort in what is now this national park. Fortunately, the Sierra Club won. Name the park.

9   Cross-country ski Grant's Grove, backpack to Rae Lakes, stay at historic Muir Hut at Muir Pass, hike Muir Trial and Pacific Crest Trial simultaneously, camp at Cedar Grove, descend canyons, snowshoe with rangers, pack-train on Glen Pass, hike over Mather Pass, and smell the wildflowers at Evolution Basin, are all exciting things to do at this national park. Name the national park.

10   Forests of giant bladder kelp, of which some leafy stems reach 200 feet above the ocean floor, surround this national park. Name the park.

11   What is the largest animal on earth and at which national park might you expect to find it?

12   "A wonderful bird is the pelican.
              Its beak can hold more food than its belly can.
              It can hold enough food in its beak,
                   to last it a week.
              I really don't know how the hell it can."
                                        Unknown Author

Pelicans are not alone among the many species of shorebirds that flourish at this national seashore. Sir Francis Drake, one of England's great 16th century sailors, stopped for a visit to this seashore, because he felt the milky-white, chalk cliffs resembled the Dover Cliffs along the coast of the English Channel.

The NPS, in its park brochure, describes this wonderful park as a place you can experience ". . . the rhythmic play of sea-spray along the coast; wings of birds flashing in flight; drifting shrouds of mist and fog; browsing deer who occasionally follow your movements with soft eyes; migrating whales offshore; and the ebb and flow of Pacific tides." And let's not overlook the lighthouse (well worth an up-close-and-personal visit), miles of shell-covered sandy beaches, the elk herd, a rich assortment of wildflowers, hundreds of California quail, beautiful butterflies, and one of the finest visitor centers in the national park service. What national seashore is this?

Western, Hawaii, Guam and American Samoa Region

Western, Hawaii, Guam
and American Samoa Region

13   This relatively new visitor center is literally located below what
        is billed as 'The World's Tallest Thermometer' . . . at 134 ft.
        high. Name the visitor center, the parks it supports, and explain
        why the thermometer is precisely 134 feet high. .

14   This national park recreation area is the closest to a
        metropolitan area and contains:
        - 116 square miles of open space,
        - 100 miles of hiking trials,
        - 79 shipwrecks,
        - 23 rare and endangered species,
        - 10 historic forts,
        - 5 lighthouses, and
        - 2 redwood forests.
        Name this national recreation area.

15   This twice-moved lighthouse is now in a coveted and secure
        place. Chinese laborers hand-dug a tunnel to provide land
        access to the new site. If you're over 5-ft. 6-in. tall you'll have
        to bend to get through the tunnel. A light-weight (no pun
        intended) suspension bridge was built to connect the rock the
        light sits on with the mainland. Although plenty safe, the bridge
        tends to sway in the wind; hence, park service volunteers stand
        by to limit passage to five persons at once. A fine specimen of
        basalt "pillow rock" lava, that millions of years ago slowly
        seeped through the ocean floor, stands beside the bridge; many
        believe it is the finest example of basalt pillow lava in the
        world. What lighthouse is this?

16   "This is the best tree-lovers monument that could possibly be
        found in all the forests of the world", said John Muir. To what
        monument was John referring?

17   The NPS describes this site as, ". . . pastoral landscape (that) is a hiker's paradise of forested canyons, tree-lined ridges, open grassy slopes and historic farm buildings. Most trials are long and steep, ascending to ridge tops for ocean views." Along its trails expect to find fields of forget-me-nots, poppies, Queen Anne's lace, morning glories, yarrow as tall as you are, and a massive variety of other wildflowers, still shining with dew in the early morning hours. What NPS site is this?

18   On a clear day, you can look from any shore point at Golden Gate National Recreation Area and see an island about 19 miles offshore. What island is it?

19   This snake frequents most of the NPS parks in this region. Name the snake. Hint: A baseball team is named after it.

20   This colorful bird has a red forehead and likes to drill nest holes in the arms and trunks of Saguaro cactus. They are a common bird at this national park. Name the bird and the park.

21   Located below a majestic bridge, this fort has its own roof-mounted lighthouse. The fort was designed to mount 126 huge muzzle-loading cannon, and house 500 army soldiers. Name the fort.

22   This plant lives to be 200 years old, but its arms don't grow-in until it is about 75 years old. Name the plant and the park where you are most likely to find it. Hint: It grows nowhere else in the world but the Sonora Desert, and its range is limited to between sea level and 4,500-feet.

23   This park has a Desert Museum nearby with its very own walk-in humming-bird aviary. Fourteen species of humming-birds are kept in a natural environment. A naturalist is always present to point out different species, tell amusing stories and answer questions. Name the park.

24   Rangers at this NPS site must move visitors away from the visitor center to clear a runway for this bird to run and take-off. Name the park site and the bird. Hint: Its wingspan is 7-feet.

Western, Hawaii, Guam and American Samoa Region

25   This memorial was built to honor those who died on December 7, 1941 when the Japanese attacked Pearl Harbor, Hawaii. Name the memorial.

26   What bird has the largest wingspan in the world?

27   A 1950s vintage Nike missile silo has been turned into a museum that is open to the public the first Sunday of every month at this NPS site: a park ranger guides visitors down into the missile silo. It is the only one of its kind in the nation. Not to worry – the missiles on display are inert and cannot be fired. Name the NPS site.

28   This NPS site has twice burned to the ground and been restored. It shares the grounds with the now defunct Sutra Baths, which in its heyday attracted thousands of visitors from San Francisco each day to enjoy indoor, saltwater, Olympic-size pools and an amusement park. Visitors arrived by narrow-gauge steam train, the railroad bed of which is now preserved as a hiking trial between the Sutra Baths and China Beach. Sutra ruins can still be seen. This popular site offers the best views of Golden Gate NRA, and the best omelets - a selection of over 30, with many vegetarian. Offshore are the notorious Seal Rocks, home to sea lions and marine birds. Name this NPS site.

29   This island in the heart of San Francisco Bay has been used as a fort, a lighthouse and a prison. It was closed as a prison in 1961 by the then US attorney general. This site incarcerated the likes of Al "Scarface" Capone, "Creepy" Karpis, "Machine Gun" Kelly and Robert Stroud. It is now managed by the NPS. Name this NPS island site, the US attorney general who closed the prison and Robert Stroud's nickname.

30   When this building was built in 1912 it was the largest steel-reinforced concrete building in the world. Name the building and the NPS site where it can be found.

31   Where was the first lighthouse on the Pacific Coast?

32   What is the nickname for Alcatraz?

33   Part A:
      In 1969, Native American political activists occupied Alcatraz
      for 19 months. They did so in the name of the "Indians of All
      Tribes". Imitating the European colonist's purchase of
      Manhattan Island from Native Indians, the "Indians of All
      Tribes" offered to buy Alcatraz from the federal government.
      How much were they willing to pay?
      Part B:
      The "Indians of All Tribes" chose Alcatraz because it reminded
      them of an Indian reservation . . . they said, "It was isolated
      from modern facilities, the soil is rocky and unproductive, and .
      . .". What was their third criterion for identifying Alcatraz with
      an Indian reservation?

34   Ninetieth-century Charcoal Kilns, Furnace Creek, Marble and
      Golden Canyons, Ubehebe Crater, The Sand Dunes, a Ghost
      Town and Telescope Peak (11,049 feet) are just a few of the
      sights to enjoy at this national park. Name the national park.
      Hint: Bring your own water.

35   This canyon hike is one of the most unique, beautiful and
      interesting . . . it includes a half-mile stretch of polished marble
      narrows. Sheer marble walls, hundreds of feet high, in vivid
      swirling patterns, form the narrows, which are wide enough for
      only two people to pass. Name the canyon.

36   The Borax Twenty-Mule Team got its reputation at this national
      park. Name the park.

37   This US president starred in a TV and radio show about Death
      Valley and the Borax Twenty-Mule Team. Name the show, the
      president and one co-star.

38   At the foot of the imposing Sierra Nevada in eastern California,
      lies the NPS historic site known as "Manzanar". What is the
      significance of this national historic site?

39   A ten-million dollar palace exists in the desert, hundreds of miles from civilization. It was built and later owned exclusively by "An ordinary one-blanket jackass prospector", as he called himself. The NPS now owns the castle – a true architectural wonder. Name the prospector, his partners and the castle's whereabouts.

40   This national monument is named after a cactus with a musical instrument for a name. Name the national monument.

41   Who said, "I got four things to live by: Don't say nothing that will hurt anybody. Don't give advice – nobody will take it anyway. Don't complain. Don't explain."?

42   In 1905, this Wild West adventurer, on a bet, set a rail speed record from Los Angeles to Chicago in 44 hours, 54 minutes – the Santa Fe Railroad cleared the tracks of all freight and limited trains so that the 'Coyote Express' could cannonball through. Who was this Wild West adventurer?

43   This great conservationist planted a fruit orchard at his estate. The estate is now managed by the NPS. Name this NHS.

44   As a commercial logging venture, harvesting giant sequoia trees has never been successful. Why not?

45   True or false? When a giant sequoia tree was struck by lightning and caught fire at the top, a park service forester climbed a nearby tree, attached a rope between them, crossed over and extinguished the fire with a hose.

46   This beautiful turquoise-blue bird has a black face and crown. It is big, noisy, friendly, and common, and frequents most Western Region parks. If you're not careful, it will fly away with your picnic groceries. Name the bird.

47   In desert parks like Mojave, Great Basin and Death Valley, vast flat dried-up areas exist where water, if and when it comes, evaporates quickly. Because these areas were once under sea, their surface has a salty-white crust. What are these areas called?

48   Racetrack Playa in California's Death Valley NP is famous for its mysterious moving __?__ What moves mysteriously?

49

> "The Desert reveals itself nakedly and cruelly,
> with no meaning but its own existence."
> Edward Abby, <u>Desert Solitaire</u>

As it has for eons, wind and water erosion continue to undress this desert park. In doing so, nature reveals slopes of colorful-layered sand and mounds of fossil remains. Name this national park. Hint: It is located on the Colorado Plateau, and antelope run wild.

50   Cochise, Geronimo and Natchez were leaders of a Native American tribe, which once occupied what is now Chiricahua NM. Name the Indian tribe.

Western, Hawaii, Guam and American Samoa Region

CHIRICAHUA NATIONAL MONUMENT

51

> "It is not enough to understand the natural world;
> the point is to defend and preserve it."
> Edward Abby, <u>A Voice Crying In The Wilderness</u>

Sometime in the 1970's this cute little fellow with yellow legs disappeared from Yosemite, Kings Canyon and Sequoia National Parks. Various amphibians have similarly disappeared. Scientists are not sure why, but believe pollution and global-scale climate change are to blame. That an animal, once fruitful and considered inexhaustible, can suddenly disappear from protected national parks leaves everyone baffled. We didn't hear Abbey; we didn't defend and preserve this animal. Name the unfortunate little critter.

52   Introduced to Hawaii in the 1800's to kill rats, this fierce hunter is wiping out native bird species in our parks and domestic farmland. Name the mammal.

53   Gold Bluffs Beach, a 7-mile stretch of dunes and sandy beach, is part of this national park. If you enjoy the sight of hundreds of old-growth trees washed up on the beach, bleach-gray old ghosts, some ten feet in diameter, this is the park for you. One of the more popular parks, it is home to Roosevelt elk, black bear, rough-skinned newts and the world's tallest tree at 367.8-feet. Name the national park. Hint: Its forest develops the world's largest volume of living matter per acre.

54   "Their veneration for old customs was a quality
            I liked in Indians." Willa Cather, <u>Death Comes to the Archbishop</u>

       For thousands of years, Native Americans lived in the redwood forests of today's Redwood NP. They traveled in redwood dug-out canoes; fished the streams and ocean; collected nuts, berries and seeds; hunted land and ocean mammals; and made the forest their shelter and home. Name one of the three principal Native American tribes that occupied Redwood NP.

55   Apache Indians terrorized white settlers passing through a narrow passage of the Chiricahua Mountains known as 'Apache Pass'. What nickname did the settlers give to Apache Pass?

56   "When I was young I walked all over this
      country, east and west, and saw no other
      people than the Apaches."
              Cochise, Apache Chief

      For 10 million dollars, the U.S. Government bought from
      Mexico 29 million acres, including Apache Pass, which became
      parts of Arizona and New Mexico. What is the purchase called?

57   Jesse James Canyon passes through this national monument.
      Name the national monument.

58   From 1857 to 1858 a stagecoach line ran through Apache Pass
      on its way from San Antonio, Texas to San Diego, California.
      What was the stage line called?

59   The U.S. Army Cavalry were sent to Apache Pass to keep it
      open, protect the settlers and mail passing through, and to
      protect what other vital resource?

60   Established in 1858, first as an Overland Mail Company stage
      station, and then as a post to guard Apache Pass, name this
      national historic site.

61   Lichens spatter the rock formations of Chiricahua National
      Monument. Lichen is a symbiotic association of what two
      organisms? Hint: The first forms of life.

62   Southeastern Arizona and southwestern New Mexico NPs are
      the only places in America where all four skunk species can be
      found together. Name any two . . . all four for extra credit.

63   Skunks are nocturnal. To be seen at night they have splotches
      of white fur. The white fur helps predators identify and steer
      clear of skunk. This pleases the predator as well as the skunk,
      because the skunk doesn't like to spray other animals . . . it
      can't stand the smell. Knowing that tidbit of trivial information,
      what did the skunk say when the wind changed direction?

64   If you ask a skunk to lend you its cell-phone it might reply . . . ?

65   Unreal, dream-like forests of rock, Easter Island-like figures, precariously balanced rocks on tiny pedestals, pinnacles aimed at space, spires to nowhere, columns to rival or, perhaps, outdo the Greeks' best work, are all examples of the rock formations to be enjoyed at this incredible national monument. Name the national monument. Hint: Often referred to as "Wonderland of Rocks" or "Land of the Standing-up Rocks."

66   In the southeast parks of Arizona, mountains rise abruptly and are isolated from one another, separated by desert seas; alienating mammals, plants, trees and insects. What is the euphemism for such natural occurrences?

67   Janice E. Bowers in her wonderful book <u>Chiricahua</u> describes a rock formation at Chiricahua NM as, "Erosion has whittled the rocks into chess pieces – pawns and castles, knights and bishops, kings and queens, all crowded together at one end of the chessboard." To what rock formation is she referring?

68   This massive plant is considered an icon of the American Southwest. Name the plant.

69   Echo Canyon Loop, Hailstone Trial, Bonita Canyon and Silver Spur Meadow Trial are enjoyable hikes at Chiricahua NM, where six biotic communities – groups of plant and animal species that normally live together - can be explored. Name any four biotic communities at Chiricahua NM.

70   Mountains southwest of the 'Heart of Rocks', Chiricahua NM, resemble the silhouette of a man facing heaven. Whose face does the mountain silhouette resemble?

71   Blue grama, side-oats grama, black grama, wolf-tail, panic and love are names of what plant family?

72   The brightly-colored Sonoran king snake, common in Arizona NP's, closely resembles the coral snake and is venomous. True or false?

73   Chihuahua whiptail lizards are solely female; they reproduce by
      parthenogenesis – without sex – young from unfertilized eggs
      are born clones of the single parent. True or false?

74   U.S. Army Cavalry soldiers at Fort Bowie each received one
      government-issued _____ rifle and one _____ revolver.
      Who sold the rifles and revolvers to the government?

75   Nine species of oak grow at Chiricahua NM or Coronado N
      MEM. Name three for warm-up; four for fun; five for a
      lollipop; six for a Clark bar; seven to stay ahead of your
      brother, sister, mother, or father . . . you know you can beat
      your friends, aunt and uncle. Your grandparents will get eight.
      Nobody gets all nine.

76   Talented, experienced Indian fighters, the U.S. Army Tenth
      Cavalry Regiment fought the Cheyenne, Arapaho and Apache.
      The Indians called them the "Buffalo Soldiers". Why?

77   This unusual, raccoon-like animal has black rings around its
      eyes and a snout like a skunk. It travels in search of food in
      bands of fifty or more, noses to the ground; they root up leaf-
      litter, old logs and forage for acorns, grubs, snakes, lizards,
      mice, just about anything that moves. Name the mammal. Hint:
      It is common in Sierra Madre, Mexico.

78   Many bird species seasonally migrate from Sierra Madre
      Occidental, Mexico into southern Arizona national parks. One
      in particular is striking with its red cap, large eyes, green body
      and yellow-striped wings. Hint: It's noisy and likes to travel in
      flocks. Name it. Name a few others and receive a tip where to
      find them.

79   Big-brown, hoary, silver-haired, western pipistrelle, pallid,
      Brazilian freetail, long-legged myotis, long-tongued, and long-
      nosed are names of what animal family? Hint: Some are
      diurnal, some are nocturnal.

80   Two agave cactus plants flower at night. Name the two agaves
      and the animal that pollinates them.

Western, Hawaii, Guam
and American Samoa Region

81   Albeit found throughout southern Arizona, this desert plant is most spectacular at Tonto NM, where it grows to its largest size. After living for many years, it sprouts a long stalk to support candelabra of red and yellow flowers. Subsequent to flowering, the stalk falls to the ground, spreading its seed yards distantly from the mother plant. Name this edible plant.

82   From Phoenix, Arizona take the 'Apache Trial', Route 88, east and you will drive one of the most scenic routes in America. It will lead you to an out-of-the-way, tranquil national monument. The drive is not for the faint-of-heart; it is a grueling, rough foray through narrow canyons and mountain passes, a good portion of the ride is on single-lane, unpaved sand, with steep drop-offs and hairpin turns. In my opinion, the finest specimens of cacti and other plant species in the southwest are found here, e.g., saguaro, cholla, ocotillo, creosote, prickly pear, agave, yucca, jojoba, mesquite, palo verde and ironwood. Your drive will take you through the Lost Dutchman, Tortilla Flats, Four Cliffs Wilderness, Canyon Lake, and over Roosevelt Dam, one of the oldest in the USA. A fine national monument with three distinct cliff dwellings awaits you at the end of your rainbow. Name this serene national monument.

83   Five distinct pre-written-history cultures existed in Southwestern America between 700 A.D. and 1450 A.D. They mysteriously disappeared between 1400 and 1450 A.D. They lived a sedentary life of farming and hunting in communities, and often built stone and clay communal houses in caves and cliffs, which came to be known as "Cliff Dwellings". Name the five prominent cultures of cliff dwellers.

84   The introduction of this crop from Mexico led to the settling-down of the "hunter-gatherer" migratory societies into a sedentary lifestyle of farming. Name the crop responsible and three ways of serving it.

85   What important benefit did the inhabitants of the Tonto Basin cliff dwellings derive from corn cobs?

86　　What is the least likely reason that scientists give for the
　　　sudden collapse and demise of the five cultures of
　　　Southwestern American cliff dwellers?
　　　A.　Abandonment due to Apache raids
　　　B.　Sudden volcanic activity that may have clouded the
　　　　　area and reduced temperatures.
　　　C.　Overall climatic change
　　　D.　Salinization of croplands or water sources
　　　E.　Internal strife
　　　F　　They migrated and were absorbed by other cultures.

87　　Specify three uses of cacti the cliff dwellers relied on?

88　　The quest in 1540 for the "Seven Cities of Cibola" – mythical
　　　cities of gold – led to the establishment of this national
　　　memorial. Name the national memorial set aside to
　　　commemorate this epic quest, and the person who led the
　　　expedition.

89　　About how many bat "hits" does an agave – century plant -
　　　bloom experience in a single night?
　　　A.　24
　　　B.　140
　　　C.　480
　　　D.　3,800

90　　A flourishing trade in a product made from the agave cactus
　　　existed between Mexico and the United States. What was the
　　　product?

91　　At Coronado N MEM, Poor Man, Dexter, Annie Mills,
　　　Montezuma, Little Maggies, Lookout, Chicago, and State of
　　　Texas are names for what?

92　　This national monument is proud of its 5-storey cliff dwelling
　　　built by the Sinague people in the 12th century. Name the
　　　monument. Hint: It is 50 miles south of Flagstaff, Arizona.

Western, Hawaii, Guam
and American Samoa Region

93   This site, part of Montezuma Castle NM, is a limestone sink
      formed by the collapse of an underground cavern. It is well
      worth a hike around the rim, down into the sink, and behind to
      the Beaver Creek, where the Sinague built an elaborate system
      of irrigation canals to water their crops. Name the site.

94   This Indian village ruin dates back to the 11th century. It sits
      high on a hill above Verde Valley. Its gregarious people traded
      salt for turquoise from Indians of the Colorado Plateau. Name
      this national monument.

95   The river people of southern Arizona, Pima Indians, welcomed
      Father Kino in 1691. It was here at this national historic site
      that Father Kino established a Jesuit Mission. The mission was
      plagued with troubles throughout its 150-year history – disease,
      revolt, killings, Apache raids, fire, internal church strife, lack of
      funds and politics all took their toll. It changed hands in 1767
      when Spain's Carlos III was crowned; he expelled the Jesuits
      and replaced them with Franciscans. Name this national
      historic park.

96   If you lived at Tuzigoot in 1300 A.D., what would you offer the
      merchant Indians, from Mexico and Colorado, in trade for their
      turquoise, shells and macaw parrots?

97   A volcano erupted here in 1064 through 1065. Today it's a ski
      resort among other things. Hundreds of cinder cones can be
      explored at this national monument: the most perfectly shaped
      is SP Crater. Name this national monument.

98   "Trade is carried on by means of pack mules, over treacherous
              trails.
          The desert has a peculiar horror; I don't mean thirst or Indian
              massacre . . .
          The very floor of the world is cracked open into countless
              canyons and arroyos."
                      Death Comes for the Archbishop, Willa Cather.

      According to Navajo Indian myth, Spider Woman lives on top
      of Spider Rock at this national monument. This national

monument preserves Native American history from the first cliff dwellers, the Anasazi, to the current occupants, the Navajo. The Anasazi built cliff houses just below the rim of this monument's majestic canyon walls. Cliff dwelling ruins from AD 350 to 1300 can be seen today. Name this national monument.

99   Oldest continuously operating Navajo Nation trading post, specializing in hand-made blankets, robes, rugs, turquoise jewelry, pottery and other arts and crafts, can be browsed at this national historic site. Name the national historic site.

100   What makes up a 'Stair-Step' canyon?

101   What is the finest example of a 'Stair-Step' canyon in the world?

102   Where is the deepest canyon in America, and how deep is it? Hint: No, it is not the Grand Canyon; in fact, don't look for it in Arizona.

103   Approximately, how deep is the Grand Canyon?

104   What are the three principal ingredients that make up the driving forces that carved, and continue to carve, the Grand Canyon?

105   How many dams are there that now dam up America's once-wild rivers?
         A = 100   B = 300   C = 500   D = more than 1,000

106   Palms are a sure sign of a source of ground water and mild winters. A palm oasis in a desert is a rare commodity; to find five such oases in the same national park is special indeed. Park guests can visit these special retreats at what national park?

107   Temple of Peace is a cluster of trees where United Nations officials from all over the world met in 1945 to honor the recently deceased US President Franklin Delano Roosevelt, the chief architect of the United Nations. They choose this place

because love of nature and its beauty is universal among all the peoples of the world. This NPS site was chosen as the place where people, unknown to one another, but joined in their love of nature, could meet and hope to find a mutual, common basis of understanding for building a foundation to solve the world's problems. On what NPS site did the United Nations choose to meet in 1945?

108   If you like large-scale models of every type of ship imaginable since the beginning of time, displayed in handsome intricate detail, then this museum is the place for you. If you like to wander through room after room of sailing and other maritime artifacts, then this surely is the national historic place for you. If you prefer to browse through the Maritime Library, you will find a comprehensive collection of sea, naval and nautical books, periodicals, 250,000 photographs and ship plans. If you like a dock with an anchored fleet of historic ships, then you just hit a home run. Name this national historic park. Hint: Home of nice oil-tanker, luxury-liner and gold-rush displays.

109   High above a major southern California city, this national recreation area is a green belt that runs perpendicular to the sea, embracing the San Gabriel Mountains. It encompasses Malibu Lagoon and other State Park beaches. Name this popular national recreation area.

110   A world-class watershed, home to rainbow trout and largemouth bass, colorful sailboats, sparkling water, old-growth forest, wildlife, and gold panning are some of the attractions at this national recreation area. For centuries, Wintu Indians enjoyed a prosperous life here. Name this relatively small and unknown national recreation area.

111   This national park includes most of South Snake Range, a superb desert community mountain island. As the elevation changes, so does the climate and the types of plants and animals that live here . . . which makes this park a great place to observe and study desert bio-geography. The park includes 13 mountain peaks above 11,000 feet, poor soil, short growing season, high winds, thin air and intense solar radiation. Limber

and bristlecone pine trees showcase here. As the NPS says in its park brochure, "Bristlecone pines are the stuff of legend. True masters of longevity, they endure not centuries but millenniums . . . A Bristlecone pine found here was determined to be the world's oldest living tree: 4,950 years of age." Name this national park. Hint: Lexington Arch and Lehman Caves are found here.

112   Best known example of glacial-carving, "the incomparable valley", a mosaic of meadows sprinkled with wild flowers, are some of the accolades sung about this busy national park. No further hint necessary . . . name this national park.

113   Flying fox, tall sea cliffs, coral reefs, volcanic islands, warm white beaches, rain forest, Pola Island visitor center and scenic drive, Vatia Valley, Afono Pass, Lake Mountain, ava bowl, song and dance are among the many surprises awaiting visitors to this national park. Name this national park. Hint: Plan on a long visit.

114   Marines of the III Amphibious Corps Artillery, U.S. Army 77th Tank Division, Assault Troops of the 3rd Marine Division, 1st Provisional Marine Brigade, and the 305th U.S. Army Regimental Combat Team joined forces, came ashore under heavy enemy bombardment, and eventually kicked the Japanese off a Pacific island. Of the 55,000 American troops involved, 7,000 lost their lives. A national historic park was established on the island to commemorate the bravery, valor and ultimate sacrifice many paid in participating and winning the campaigns of the Pacific theater of World War II. Name this solemn national historic park.

115   Where is War in the Pacific National Historic Park?

116   This national monument features two ancient, 1300 A.D., Pueblo-people cliff dwellings in remarkably good condition – Betatakin and Keet Seel. To view Betatakin, hike an easy trial to an overlook; for a closer look take a park ranger-guided tour – limited to 25 per day. To view Keet Seel you will need a back-country permit – limited to 20 per day. A third cliff

Western, Hawaii, Guam and American Samoa Region

dwelling, Inscription House, is closed due to its vulnerability. Horseback riding through the monument's magnificent canyons is a real treat. Name this national monument.

117   A huge reservoir, behind the first dam ever built on the Colorado River, is the 110-mile-long home of this national recreation area. Name the national recreation area.

118   Hot lava cooled and cracked into hexagonal-shaped basalt columns that resemble a stack of pencils without erasers. John Muir and Pacific Crest Trials criss-cross at this national monument. Rainbow Falls (101-foot drop) and Soda Springs, naturally carbonated mineralized springs, are a nice easy day hike from the visitor center. Name this national monument.

119   Which play, of those listed below, is not one of Eugene O'Neill's four Pulitzer Prize-winning plays.
        A.   Beyond the Horizon
        B.   Anna Christie
        C.   Ah Wilderness!
        D.   Long Day's Journey into Night

120   Events of July 17, 1944 forever changed deep-seated US Navy policy, procedures and practices. On this evening, two US Navy munitions cargo ships were being loaded with thousands of tons of explosives when a terrible explosion took place. The SS Bryan and SS Quinault, piers, and structures on the piers, disintegrated. It was reported, "The largest remaining pieces of the ships found were the size of a suitcase". The blast smashed buildings and rail cars near the piers, and damaged most buildings in the nearest town. All 320 men on duty were killed. Safety practices were ignored because they weren't fast enough. Reflecting the racial segregation of the day, an all-black Navy crew had been assigned the dangerous duty of loading the two ships . . . they were all killed. Two weeks later, a new all-black crew were ordered to load replacement ships . . . 258 men refused. Of these 258, 208 were summarily court-martialed and dishonorably discharged. To set an example, the remaining 50 were singled out for general courts-martial on the grounds of mutiny, and received eight-to-fifteen years at hard

labor. Some good came out of the sacrifice these men made, for on July 26, 1948, President Harry S Truman ordered the armed forces to desegregate, and new safety standards for handling ordnance were implemented. The 258 men were granted presidential clemency and given honorable discharges. Where did this dark day in America history take place and is there a national memorial?

121   This park has a turbulent past. Nature and man's activities have been violent. For a million years nature has spewed forth lava, gases and cinders, creating interesting, but rugged, terrain. At this park site, three Modoc Indian chiefs, including the most famous of all –Captain Jack – were hung by the U.S. Cavalry for repeated altercation, with resultant bloodshed, and refusing to settle on a government reservation. On a happier note, park rangers at the visitor center provide lanterns for exploring lava tubes. It is an unusual and fun place – name the park.

122   "What is there for you in the birds, birds, birds
                crying down on the North wind in September,
                acres of birds spotting the air going south?
                Is there something finished?
                And some new beginning on the way?"
                                                Falltime, Carl Sandburg

        Lower Klamath Falls National Wildlife Refuge, Tule Lake NWR and Clear Lake NWR are all surrounding neighbors to this national monument. And they are home to about eight million waterfowl during the fall migration, which peaks approximately the second week of November. Watching these magnificent birds come and go in mass flight is an incredible sight. See it at least once in a lifetime. Name the friendly neighbor NM.

123   A monument stands, under the watchful eye of the NPS, to honor this European who was the first to set foot on the west coast of what is now the United States. Name this national monument and state the explorer's nationality.

124 One look and you know at once how this national monument got its name . . . abrupt rock formations dominate the surrounding rolling hills. Strenuous, but at the same time enjoyable, hikes up steep cliffs provide excellent views for miles around. Name this national monument. Hint: San Andreas Rift Zone is responsible.

125 At this national park on Maui, visitors can hike a rain forest and a cinder-cone volcano in a single day. Name this national park.

126 Historic Hansen's disease (leprosy) colony is preserved at this park. Name the national historic park.

127 Once known as City of Refuge National Park, until 1819 it was a sanctuary for vanquished warriors. What is it called today?

128 Traditional native Hawaiian activities and culture are demonstrated and preserved for future generations at this national historic park on the Island of Hawaii. Name this national historic park.

129 What group of religious pioneers built a fort over the main spring and established a cattle ranch operation at Pipe Spring National Monument, Arizona?

130 Casa Grande at Casa Grande Ruins National Monument, Arizona is what?
A. Prehistoric tar pit
B. Dried up lake bed
C. 650 year old, 4-storey building
D. None of the above

131 Twelfth-century Pueblo Indians built side and front walls to create cliff dwellings at existing limestone alcoves. Name the national monument where this took place.

132 Wupatki National Monument in Arizona preserves the ruins of what two farming people?

CHAPTER 5 –
WESTERN, HAWAII, GUAN and
AMERICAN SAMOA REGION
Answers

1   Channel Islands, NP.

2   Hawaii Volcanoes NP; Kilauea Volcano.

3   Sequoia, Muir Woods and Redwoods NPs.

4   Eugene O'Neill . . . perhaps America's greatest playwright;
     Eugene O'Neill NHS, Danville, California . . . his estate and
     Tao House, outside of San Francisco, are well worth seeing.

5   John Muir at the west entrance to Yosemite NP . . . A plaque is
     there to commemorate the event,

6   His pet Dalmatian – Blemie.
     Sidebar – Blemie's death deeply pained Eugene and Carlotta.
     Eugene, inspired by his grief, wrote a beautiful poem, "The
     Last Will and Testament of Silverdene Emblem O'Neill" as
     tribute, which the NPS has respectfully mounted on a placard at
     the grave site. In my opinion, every pet owner would enjoy
     reading the poem.

7   Lassen Peak; Lassen Volcanic NP, California.

8   Sequoia NP, California.

9   Kings Canyon NP, California/

10   Channel Islands NP.

11   The endangered blue whale; It can be seen off Channel Islands
        NP.
        Sidebar – The blue whale was hunted to near-extinction
        because it contained large quantities of oil and, more
        importantly, did not sink, but floated, when killed . . . making
        recovery of the oil easier.

12   Point Reyes NS, California.

13   NPS Mojave Desert Information Center, Baker, California
        provides ranger interpretive services about Mojave Desert,
        Death Valley NP and newly formed Mojave Desert Preserve.
        The height of 134 feet is to commemorate the highest
        temperature recorded in North America . . . 134°F, Death
        Valley, 1913.

14   Golden Gate NRA, San Francisco, CA.

15   Point Bonita Lighthouse is at the entrance to the Golden Gate
        and inside Marin Headlands, a unit of Golden Gate NRA.
        Sidebar – Known to few, NPS volunteers conduct a ranger
        interpretive walk to the lighthouse every weekend at about
        noontime. Call Marin Headlands visitor center (415) 331-1540
        or check the NPS internet site at www.nps.gov/goga for more
        information.

16   Muir Woods NM, California.

17   Olema Valley, a unit of Golden Gate NRA, California.

18   Farallon National Wildlife Refuge.

19   Diamondback rattle-snake; expect to find it at Joshua Tree,
        Kings and Sequoia, Grand Canyon, Saguaro, Tonto,
        Montezuma, Navajo, Painted Desert, Canyon de Chelly, Organ
        Pipe and Tuzigoot National Parks, to name a few.

20   Gila woodpecker; Saguaro NP, Tucson, Arizona.

21   Fort Point, a unit of Golden Gate NRA, is located on the San
      Francisco side of Golden Gate Bridge, and well worth a visit.

22   Saguaro cactus; Saguaro NP, Tucson, Arizona.

23   Saguaro NP, Tucson, Arizona.

24   Puukohola Heiau NHS, Hawaii Island – "The Big Island";
      Laysan albatross.

25   USS Arizona Memorial.
      Sidebar – The NPS provides a shuttle boat to take visitors to
      the memorial, which has been placed directly over the USS
      Arizona. The hull can be seen. Most of the 1,177 crewmen who
      lost their lives in the fight for freedom are entombed there.
      Their names are inscribed on the marble wall of the memorial.

26   The wandering albatross has a wingspan of 11 feet. Sorry, it is
      not found in North America; you can find it south of the
      Equator.

27   Nike Missile Site is at Marin Headlands, a unit of Golden Gate
      NRA, San Francisco, CA.

28   Cliff House, a unit of Golden Gate NRA, San Francisco, CA.

29   Alcatraz Island is a unit of Golden Gate NRA; Robert F.
      Kennedy closed the prison because of the immense cost of
      upkeep and operation; Robert Stroud kept canaries in his cell at
      Leavenworth Penitentiary, but never had birds at Alcatraz.
      Nevertheless, he got the nickname, "the Birdman of Alcatraz".
      Sidebar - Although he loved birds, Stroud disliked people and
      could not get along with other prisoners. He spent his entire
      stay at Alcatraz in solitary confinement. To visit Alcatraz you
      must take a ferry from Pier 41 at Fisherman's Wharf, SF. It is
      suggested you make reservations a few days in advance, for this
      is a very popular site. The NPS self-guided audio tour of the
      cell block is extremely interesting. Call (415) 556-0560 for
      ferry reservations, and visit Alcatraz on the web at
      www.nps.gov/alcatraz.

30   The Cellhouse; Alcatraz – Golden Gate NRA, San Francisco, CA.

31   Alcatraz Island - Golden Gate NRA, San Francisco, CA.
        Sidebar – Alcatraz Lighthouse was built in 1854 as a result of the heavy California gold rush traffic.

32   "The Rock"

33   Part A – The "Indians of All Tribes" offered to pay the same amount as the Europeans paid for Manhattan – $24 in beads, colored cloth and other trinkets.
        Part B – Like many an Indian reservation, Alcatraz does not support game; therefore, there is no hunting.

34   Death Valley NP, California and Nevada

35   Mosaic Canyon Trial, Death Valley NP, California and Nevada.

36   Death Valley NP, California and Nevada.

37   Death Valley Days; Ronald Reagan, 40th US President; Co-stars included Clint Eastwood and Carol O'Connor.
        Sidebar – Death Valley Days was an award-winning series that made broadcasting history by running for 35 years.

38   Manzanar NHS was one of ten camps at which Japanese-American citizens were interned during World War II.

39   Walter F. Scott or simply "Scotty" as he preferred to be called. Bessie and Albert Johnson funded "Scotty's Castle", as it came to be known, and lived there with Scotty, intermittently, for ten years. Scotty's Castle is a unit of Death Valley NP, California and Nevada.

40   Organ Pipe Cactus NM, Arizona.

41   "Scotty" of Scotty's Castle, a unit of Death Valley NP, California and Nevada.

42   "Scotty" of Scotty's Castle, a unit of Death Valley NP, California and Nevada.

43   John Muir NHS, Martinez, California.

44   When sequoias hit the ground they split and shatter into small, unusable pieces.

45   True . . . This happened at Sequoia National Park in 1967 to the 'California' giant sequoia tree.

46   Steller's jay.
      Sidebar – Steller's jay prefers conifer forests. It is named for the German naturalist Georg Wilhelm Steller, who accompanied Vitus Bering when he "discovered" Alaska in 1741.

47   Playas.

48   Stones and boulders - Ostensibly, when no one is looking dozens of stones and boulders (the largest weighed-in at 700 lb.) trek across the desert floor, leaving behind shallow, arcane trials . . . the largest track is 1,982-ft long. They are moved by the wind dragging a shallow sheet of ice which holds the boulders: the ice moves with sufficient force to shear off fence posts.

49   Painted Desert – a unit of Petrified Forest NP, Navajo, Arizona.

50   Apache.

51   Foothill yellow-legged frog.

52   Indian mongoose.

53   Redwood NP, California.

54   Yurok and Tolowa groups still exist, Chilula were absorbed into an inland tribe.

55   Pass of Chance.

56   The Gadsden Purchase.

57   Chiricahua National Monument, Arizona.

58   'Jackass Mail', it latter became Butterfield Overland Mail.

59   Apache Springs – the only year-round reliable source of water, in an area surrounded by the Sonora Desert to the west and the Chihuahuan Desert to the east.

60   Fort Bowie NHS, Arizona.

61   Algae and fungus – algae provide the food, fungus the attachment and protection.

62   Striped, spotted, hooded and hog-nosed skunks

63   "It's all coming back to me now."

64   "Sorry, it's out of odor."

65   Chiricahua NM, Arizona.

66   'Islands in the Sky' or simply, 'Sky Islands.'

67   Heart of Rocks, Chiricahua NM, Arizona.

68   Saguaro cactus; Saguaro NP, Arizona.
       Sidebar – Saguaro grow to over 4,000 pounds and live for more
       than 200 years; they first grow their infamous arms at about
       age 75.

69   Meadow, riparian forest, chaparral, conifer forest, mixed pine-
       oak woodland, oak woodland.

70   Cochise, Chief of the Apaches.

71   Plains grass.

72   False – it is innocuous.

73   True.

74   Springfield sold the rifles; Colt provided the revolvers.

75   Gambel, emory, net-leaf, silver-leaf, Arizona white, sandpaper,
       Mexican blue, toumey and shrub oak.

76   U.S. Army Tenth Calvary was an all-black regiment. The
       Indians thought their black curly hair reminded them of a
       buffalo head.

77   Coatimundis.

78   Thick-billed parrot; other birds from Mexico include: red-faced
       and olive warbler, Mexican spotted owl, Mexican chickadee,
       hepatic tanager, the elegant and eared trogons, and several
       humming-birds – magnificent, white-eared, Lucifer and
       beryline. These birds cannot be found anywhere else in the

United States. Some may be seen in the aviaries at the Desert Museum, Tucson, adjacent to Saguaro NP, Arizona.

79   Bats.

80   Palmer agave and Parry agave; pollinated by bats; both are found at Tonto NM and Chiricahua NM, Arizona.

81   Agave cactus, known as the century plant.

82   Tonto NM, Roosevelt, AZ.

83   Anasazi, Mogollon, Salado, Hohokam and Sinague.
      Sidebar – The NPS puts on a great slide show about the Hohokam and Salado cliff dwellers at the Tonto NM visitor center. In my opinion, it is one of the best slide shows in the NPS system.

84   Corn, sometimes referred to as maize; plain corn on the cob, or ground and made into mush or baked into more palatable bread, dumplings, or griddle-cakes.

85   They dried them in the sun and burned them. They were a significant source of fuel.

86   Correct answer is A – Evidence proves Apaches did not arrive in the Southwest until 1500 A.D.

87   Food, drink, tools, sandals, mats, baskets, rope, nets, snares, soap, shampoo, candy, dye, firewood, weapons, and carrying sticks.

88   Coronado N MEM, Arizona; Francisco Vazquez de Coronado.

89   Correct answer is D - Researchers wearing night vision goggles sat under an agave bloom one night and counted 3,800 visits by bats from a nearby cave at Coronado N MEM.

90   Mescal, a powerful liquor, but illegal in the US.

91   Copper, silver, lead or zinc mines.

92   Montezuma Castle NM.

93   Montezuma Well, a unit of Montezuma Castle NM, Arizona.
      Sidebar – The trail is interesting; inside the sink you will
      discover crude pit-houses built into rock depressions, a spring
      that disappears into a cliff wall and resurfaces on the other side,
      leaches and shrimp. Maybe you'll have the good fortune to
      come across a 93-year old park volunteer who sits under the
      largest sycamore tree in Arizona and sings sonnets . . . We did.
      And Beaver Creek is full of lurking black trout.

94   Tuzigoot NM, Clarkdale, Arizona.
      Sidebar – Although a bit out-of-the-way, this park is worth a
      visit. The visitor center is an old hacienda with a fine museum,
      staffed by friendly and knowledgeable native Americans.

95   Tumacacori NHP, Arizona.

96   Copper ore, salt and woven cotton goods.

97   Sunset Crater Volcano NM Flagstaff, Arizona.

98   Canyon de Chelly NM, near Chinle, Arizona.

99   Hubbell Trading Post NHS, Ganado, Arizona.

100   Alternating layers of hard rock – granite or gneiss – and softer
      rock – siltstone or shale.
      Sidebar – Hard rock eroded by wind and rain forms steep,
      straight-walled canyons; soft rock erodes to form walls more
      gently sloped.

101   Grand Canyon NP, Grand Canyon, Arizona.

102   Hell Canyon, Snake River, Oregon-Idaho boarder; 8,000-feet deep.

103   6,000 feet deep.

104   Water, sand and gravity.

105   Correct answer is D.

106   Joshua Tree NP, Twentynine Palms, California.

107   John Muir NM, San Francisco, California.

108   San Francisco Maritime NHP, Fishermen's Wharf – San Francisco, California.

109   Santa Monica Mountains NRA, Los Angeles, California.

110   Whiskeytown-Shasta-Trinity NRA, California.

111   Great Basin NP, Nevada.

112   Yosemite NP, California.

113   National Park of American Samoa.

114   War in the Pacific NHP.

115   Guam.
       Sidebar – There are seven NHP units on the island. At the two
       assault beach sites, Asan and Agat, scuba diving and snorkeling
       to sunken U.S. military equipment and vessels is allowed. At
       the Asan Inland Unit Visitor Center, rangers provide a map and
       guidance to nine of the most popular scuba and snorkeling
       locations. Other NPS park units on the island display war-
       related structures and gun encasements, e.g., Japanese coastal
       defense guns at Piti Village.

116   Navajo National Monument, Kayenta, Arizona.

117   Lake Mead NRA, Boulder City, Nevada.

118   Devils Postpile NM, Mammoth Lakes, California.
       Sidebar – Caution: During the peak tourist season you must
       take a shuttle bus to the visitor center from the Mammoth
       Mountain Inn.

119   Correct answer is C.

120   Port Chicago Naval Magazine, Concord Naval Weapons
       Station, California; Yes, however, access to Port Chicago Naval
       Magazine National Memorial is limited and only by special
       appointment. Call (925) 838-5591.

121   Lava Beds NM, Northern California.

122   Lava Beds NM, Northern California.

123   Cabrillo NM, San Diego, California; He was the last of the
       great Spanish explorers.

124   Pinnacles NM, California.

125   Haleakala NP, Hawaii.

Western, Hawaii, Guam
and American Samoa Region

126   Kalaupapa NHP, Molokai, Hawaii.

127   Pu'uhonua NHP, Hawaii.

128   Kaloko-Honokohau NHP, Hawaii.

129   Mormons (Latter Day Saints.)

130   Correct answer is C.

131   Walnut Canyon NM, Flagstaff, Arizona.

132   Sinagua and Anasazi.

Westerm, Hawaii, Guam
and American Samoa Region

CHAPTER 6 -
SOUTHEAST, PUERTO RICO AND
VIRGIN ISLANDS REGION
Questions and Answers

A LAND RICH IN ...

NATIONAL SEASHORES ...

HISTORIC SITES ...

REVOLUTION and CIVIL WAR BATTLEFIELDS

The NPS Southeast Region consists of eight states – Kentucky,
Tennessee, North and South Carolina, Mississippi, Alabama, Georgia
and Florida – Puerto Rico and the Virgin Islands.

CHAPTER 6 -
SOUTHEAST, PUERTO RICO, AND
VIRGIN ISLANDS REGION
Questions

1   During the Civil War, a great iron-clad battleship was torpedoed and sunk by the Confederates. It has been resurfaced and is on exhibit at this national battlefield park. Name the ship and the park at which it is exhibited.

2   "Stand at the Gap and watch the procession of civilization, Marching single file – the buffalo following the trail to the Salt springs, the Indian, the fur-trader and hunter, the Cattle-raiser, the pioneer-farmer – and the frontier has passed."

Fredrick Jackson Turner, 1893

Daniel Boone, great American pioneer and frontiersmen, found a gap (to which Mr. Turner so eloquently refers above) through the Appalachian Mountains to convenience wagon trains heading west. This "Gap" has been designated a national historical park. Name the national park and the three states in which it resides.

In 1767 this area was explored by Daniel Boone, who led settlers over the Wilderness Trail through the Cumberland Gap. Became a State in 1792.

3   On April 12, 1861, the South fired on this fort, which prompted President Lincoln to call on Federal troops to put down the rebellion . . . resulting in four bloody years of civil war. Name the fort, which is today a national monument.

4   This national seashore is blessed with four operating lighthouses. Visitors can inspect the lighthouses, each with its own visitor center and unique Passport cancellation, and museums. Name this national seashore . . . for extra credit, name the lighthouses, the years they were put into service, and their height.

5   Sky, sea, shells, sand, dunes, grasslands, birds and wild ponies adorn this national seashore. It is also home to a magnificent lighthouse and a ghost-town. Loggerhead sea turtles – a threatened species – thrive in the waters off its shore. Humans are scarce, cars are forbidden, birds are everywhere, especially during spring and fall migration. Name this beautiful national seashore.

6   Here on July 14 and 15, 1864, 14,000 Union troops under the command of General A.J. Smith clashed with and defeated 9,000 Confederate cavalry under the command of General S.D. Lee. This Union victory helped protect the railroad hauling supplies to General Sherman's Atlanta Campaign. What national battlefield is this?

7   The Wright Brothers painstakingly and with much patience learned to fly on a stretch of beach on the Outer Banks of North Carolina. At what town is the Wright Brothers National Memorial located – where Orville Wright took the epochal 'first flight'?
A. Kill Devil Hills
B. Kitty Hawk
C. Nags Head
D. Cape Hatteras

8   This cave has the longest underground passages in the world at 180 miles. There are areas still unexplored. Name the cave.

9   Once a 19th-century coastal fort and then a prison, this national park site encompasses a chain of seven islands in the midst of 100 square miles of coral gardens, shoals and deep blue sea. It is now home to marine and migratory birdlife, most notably the sting-ray, brown and masked booby and several terns, including the sooty tern which breeds on the islands. After John Wilkes Booth shot President Lincoln, he jumped from the balcony to the stage and broke his leg. Dr. Mudd, innocently, set Booth's leg and, consequently, was tried by a military court, which did not honor his civil rights and convicted him of treason. Dr. Mudd was falsely imprisoned for life at this national park. Years later he was released, after he put himself in peril by saving the lives of many other prisoners stricken with the dangerously contagious yellow fever. Name the national park.

10   "I am a 300 year old (Loggerhead) turtle,
     Sleeping eating, eating sleeping,
     Blinking and easy, sleepy-eyed and easy,
     While Shakespeare writes a flock of plays,
     While John Bunyan sits in jails and writes a book,
     While Cromwell, Napoleon, Lincoln, Wilson, Lenin come and go,
     I sleep, forget, remember, forget again and ask:
     What of it?
     Don't bother me brother.
     Don't bother a dozing turtle
     Born to contemplate and yawn."

                    From Honey and Salt by Carl Sandburg

Carl knew the ways of the loggerhead turtles, who seem to live forever. And he knew the ways of peaceful seashores. The NPS, in its free brochure, describes this national seashore as follows:

"Forests so quiet that you can hear yourself breathe, sunlight filtered and diffused through over-arching trees and vines, sounds of animals scurrying in the underbrush, the gentle splash of water moving through the salt marsh, the courting bellow of the alligator, blinding light on water and sand as you emerge from the shadows of the live oak forest, a standing row of slave cabin chimneys, fallow gardens, and crumbling walls of mansions from by-gone eras. Sandpipers dance before the rhythmic advance and retreat of the sea. An osprey may dive into a wave before your eyes, and a few seconds later appear with a mullet in its talons. Loggerhead turtles, ancient reptiles of the sea, lumber ashore on deserted beaches at night. Guided by instinct, they lay their eggs and then return to the sea. Hatchlings emerge about 60-days later and scurry for the protection of the surf" . . . half to be eaten by predators.

Name this peaceful national seashore. Hint: Plum Orchard Mansion, a Georgian Revival- style mansion built in 1898, was donated to the National Park Foundation by the Andrew Carnegie family. It is located on this island seashore.

11   This national monument is the last stand of old-growth, river-bottom hardwood forest on the East Coast. It is home to a diversity of animals, including the shy pileated woodpecker, great blue herons, dragonflies, insects, spiders, toads and frogs. Name this swampy national monument.

12   What type of shoes do frogs wear in Congaree Swamp NM?

13   The panther can still be spotted in what national park?

14   Called the engineers of the Everglades, this animal supports ecological balance by digging holes in which to hide, which fills with water and help marsh snails, frogs and small fish find a home during dry spells. Name the animal.

15   What happens to frogs that illegally park in an alligator's hole?

16   "Wholly valueless", cried Florida politicians, "Time to ditch, dike and drain the swamp", they insisted.
The Everglades would be nothing but housing tracks and strip malls if it were not for the gallant, tireless efforts of this eloquent spokesperson and graceful writer. Who was this special friend of the Everglades?

Southeast, Puerto Rico and Virgin Islands Region

17   With the Holocaust Memorial Museum in Washington D.C. perhaps the sole exception, this national historic site contains the finest prison museum in the world. Name the national historic site.

18   Why did the bee go south for the winter?

19   This aquatic national park is home to the only living coral reef in America. Its beauty is found mostly underwater, for it is 95% covered by water. Name the national park. Hint: Chevrolet car name.

20   Turtle Mound Historic Site is a unit of this national seashore. The sea turtle nests here, while 300 species of birds fly overhead. Name the national seashore. Hint: Spaceships do not launch here.

21   This peanut farmer and man of integrity became president of the United States. His campaign office, home and school are units of this national historic site. He also won the Nobel Peace Prize in 2002. Name the president and national historic site.

22   Established during the Civil War, this national historic site once housed 45,000 Union soldiers. Lack of food, clothing and medical care, 1,000's died from disease, poor sanitation, lack of clean potable water, malnutrition and eventual starvation. Living in torn and battered pup tents (those fortunate to have shelter . . . most slept huddled together on bare ground), in over-crowded conditions, with no real protection from the elements, many more died from exposure. Profuse suffering and starvation led one Union sergeant to write, "I should gloery to describe this hell on Earth where it takes 7 of its occupants to make a Shadow." Overall 13,000 died from February, 1864 to May, 1865. They are buried at this site. Monuments for each of the Union companies have been erected to honor and commemorate the sacrifice of Americans who suffered captivity or, worse, lost their lives in such camps. Name the national historic site where this horrific event took place.

23   Following the siege of Atlanta, Union forces reached
        Andersonville, released the few remaining prisoners – most had
        been transferred to South Carolina or coastal Georgia – and
        captured the Confederate commander of Andersonville, Captain
        Henry A. Wirz, and some of his troops. What, if any,
        punishment did Wirz receive for the inhuman treatment of
        prisoners at Andersonville?

24   National Geographic magazine includes the white-sandy
        beaches of this national park in its list of the 10 most beautiful
        beaches in the world. Name the national park. Hint: It contains
        a tropical forest.

25   What is the main attraction of San Juan National Historic Site,
        San Juan, Puerto Rico? Hint: Check out Puerto Rico's license
        plates.

26   Nationally renowned poet, famous biographer, Pulitzer Prize
        winning author, folksinger, lecturer and historian – can you
        guess this talented person? No! How about some more hints:
        his wife raised champion dairy goats on their 245-acre farm
        named Connemara; over 5,000 books fill bookshelves
        throughout the 22-room house, including the stairwells; barns,
        sheds, rolling meadows, trout ponds, and mountainside woods
        are all found on this national historic site. Name the national
        historic site which bears the great man's name.

27   "One of the smaller blackbirds chitters on a stalk.
                And a spot of red is on its shoulder.
                And I never heard its name in my life."
                        Laughing Corn, Carl Sandburg

        Can you help Carl out . . . what is the common name of his
        blackbird?

28   Once home to the 'Lost Colony' of the late 16th century, now a
        depression in the ground is all that remains of this historic
        community.
            Queen Elizabeth I authorized 500 men to set sail for Virginia
        in seven ships commanded by Sir Richard Greenville. Name

Southeast, Puerto Rico and Virgin Islands Region

this national historic site where Virginia Dare was born – first English child born in the New World. Hint: The site isn't too inspiring, but its Elizabethan Gardens neighbor is.

29   Sir Richard Grenville was a cousin of the noble Englishman who brokered the establishment of the Roanoke Colonies in the New World. This noble Englishman was a cherished friend of Queen Elizabeth I, but not too friendly with her successor, James I, who had him beheaded. Who was this well-known nobleman?

30   General Nathanael Greene commanded the southern Continental Army during the American Revolution.
On May 21, 1781, he led the 'Patriots' against the 'Loyalists' in an unsuccessful siege of the town of Ninety Six. With the help of a European siegecraft wizard, the Patriots built a tower 30 feet high, and dug a series of parallel and zigzag approach trenches to the Loyalists' fort. The Patriots could not break into Ninety Six Fort or discourage the Loyalists into surrender, so they abandoned the effort. What is the name of the siegecraft wizard, and what was the shape of the fort?
    Hints: 1) His home in Philadelphia is a national memorial, and a bridge there bears his name. 2) Check the sky.

31   Slaves were used to dig siege trenches. What was the military term for trench diggers?

32   On February 27, 1776, Loyalists charged across a dilapidated wooden bridge shouting a war chant, "King George and Broadswords". Just beyond the bridge lay an ambush of Patriots with hidden cannons and muskets ready to fire. As they crossed the bridge shots rang out, and dozens of Loyalists and their commanders fell. "Stunned, out-gunned and leaderless . . ." the Loyalists surrendered. Where did this take place?

33   At this national battlefield on January 17, 1781, Daniel Morgan led to victory backwoods militia – "Continentals" – against a larger force of superior, trained "British regulars", led by Banastre Tarleton. Name this national battlefield?

Southeast, Puerto Rico and Virgin Islands Region

34   Kings Mountain NPS site is home to:
        A. A 19th century amusement park
        B. A native American encampment
        C. A Civil War battlefield
        D. A Revolutionary War battlefield

35   At the Battle of Guilford Courthouse this renowned commander
        ordered his artillery to fire grapeshot into the melée, on friend
        and foe alike. Who was the dirty pool player? Hint: Seven
        months later he surrendered his command.

36   At Great Smoky Mountains National Park, North Carolina and
        Tennessee, the Ocoee Super-group is hard rock made up of
        gneisses, schists and what other main ingredient?

37   Home to wild turkey (not the hooch) and hog, pipe-vine
        swallowtail, Carolina silver-bell, gypsy moths, painted trillium,
        pale jewel-weed, lady's slipper, fire pink, red fox, bobcat and
        black bear this national park was authorized by Congress in
        1926. The Cherokee described its mountains as 'shaconage'.
        Name this national park.

38   What are pipe-vine swallowtails and red spotted purples?

39   "A bear can climb a tree faster
              than a man can fall out of one."
                        Anonymous

Southeast, Puerto Rico and
Virgin Islands Region

Black bears are poached for their gall bladders and wild ginseng roots are dug up, both to be sold illegally to Asian markets for their supposed aphrodisiac attribute. This goes on today at what national park? (Just let me catch 'em!)

40 At what NP are you likely to see trees full of white wood storks or pink roseate spoonbills, in season? You are also likely to see the endangered whooping crane or sand hill crane.

41 Which food item is not part of a black bear's natural diet at Great Smoky Mountains NP?
    A. Acorns
    B. Black cherries
    C. Squawroot
    D. Corn

42 Answer the following questions, true or false:
    A. Bears hibernate. _____
    B. Great Smoky Mountains NP bear population, before it became a park, was 50 bears; today its bear population has grown, under the watchful eye of the NPS, to more than 1700 bears, crowded at two bears per square mile. _____
    C. In America, there are more black bears than grizzly and polar bears combined. _____
    D. Great Smoky Mountains NP bears came from Russia, eons ago, by crossing the Bering Land Bridge into Alaska. _____
    E. Chestnut trees, once an important source of food for bears, are all but wiped-out at Great Smoky Mountains NP because of a blight brought from Europe. _____

43 During a "sardine survey" what do park rangers hang from trees to attract bears?

44 What are "Black" Bill Walker and "Old Death" famous for at Great Smoky Mountains NP?

45   "There are no other Everglades in the world. They are, they
      have always been, one of the unique regions of the earth,
      remote, never wholly known. Nothing anywhere else is like
      them: their vast glittering openness, wider than the enormous
      visible round of the horizon, the racing free saltiness and
      sweetness of their massive winds, under the dazzling blue
      heights of space. They are unique also in the simplicity,
      diversity, the related harmony of the forms of life they enclose.
      The miracle of the light pours over the green and brown
      expanse of saw grass and of water, shining and slow-moving
      below, the grass and water that is the meaning and the central
      fact of the Everglades of Florida."
      The Everglades River of Grass, 1947, Marjory Stoneman Douglas.

      This national preserve is home to the endangered Florida
      panther, red-cockaded woodpecker and thousands of cypress
      trees. Its 728,000-acre watershed protects the Everglades. Name
      this important national preserve and make Marjory proud.

46   A tailor before becoming president, this gentleman was asked
      by Abraham Lincoln to be governor of Tennessee during the
      Civil War. His home was confiscated by the Confederate Army
      and turned into a hospital. You can visit his home at this
      national historic site. Name the president and the national
      historic site.

47   Castillo de San Marcos National Monument is a fort built to
      watch over Matanzas Bay on the land Juan Ponce de Leon
      named La Florida. Whom was the fort first built to protect?

48   Over the course of two centuries, three fortifications guarded
      the shores off South Carolina at this national monument.
      Typical weapons representing the state-of-art at the heyday of
      each fort are on display. Its 171-year history saw activity during
      the Revolutionary War, Civil War, WWI and WWII. Name this
      Fort. Hint: It was named after a Revolutionary War hero.

49   Fort Caroline National Memorial was the first fort built in the
      new world, to protect what European nation?

Southeast, Puerto Rico and Virgin Islands Region

50   Spanish explorers in 1565 captured and then massacred first one French legion, then another. The Spanish darkened the La Florida beaches with the blood of 234 French sailors. The beach and new Spanish fort became known as 'slaughters' in Spanish. Name this national monument.

51   Union Captain Quincy A. Gilmore advanced to brigadier general for his boldness in trying a new weapon that defeated the Confederates in 30 hours at Fort Pulaski. What new weapon did he try?

52   This fort was built on Cockspur Island to protect the river approaches to Savannah, Georgia in the mid-19th century. Rifled cannon pounded the fort and bored holes clear through; thus, it was surrendered to the Union in the early days of the Civil War. Name this fort national monument.

53   A few bridges, gorges and cliffs highlight life passing through this wild and scenic river system. Three river tributaries – Daddy's Creek, Clear Creek and Emory River – join a main artery that bears the name of this wild and scenic river system. Name the wild and scenic river.

54   Moose Creek National Battlefield preserves the hallowed ground on which Americans died protecting freedom during what war?

55   Stone River National Battlefield was established to commemorate one of the most significant and bloody battles of what war on American soil?

56   Name the famous scenic parkway that follows the Appalachian Mountains for approximately 470 miles through Virginia and North Carolina.

57   Booker T. Washington became the first principal of a newly formed normal school for negroes here. George Washington Carver, famous for his crop-rotation experiences and revolutionary agricultural ideas, joined the faculty. What is the name of this national historic (school) site?

58   An all-black Air Corps unit that flew many brave missions in
      WWII is honored at this national historic site. Name the
      national historic site.

59   True or false . . . Russell Cave National Monument near
      Bridgeport, Alabama was inhabited by "first Americans" for
      about 10,000 years.

60   The nation's longest mountain-top river and the southeast's
      deepest canyon can be explored at this national preserve. Name
      this national preserve.

61   General Andrew Jackson led his Tennessee Army regulars,
      militia and native American allies to victory against the Creek
      Indians at what battle?

62   Snee Farm was home to what 18th-19th century American
      politician who is best remembered for his work helping to write
      the US Constitution?

63   One hundred thousand Confederate and Union troops clashed
      at this military park in the fall of 1863. The battle ended in the
      fall of "the gateway to the deep south". Name this national
      military park.

64   This Georgia national recreation area has 16 units along a 48-
      mile course with equally good fishing, hiking, picnicking and
      boating. Name this national recreation area.

65   James Edward Oglethorpe founded a Georgia colony on St.
      Simon's Island, where he had a fort built. What is the name of
      that fort?

66   General William Sherman met Confederate General Joseph
      Johnson for combat at this mountain battlefield near Atlanta.
      Name this national battlefield park.

67   Ocmulgee National Monument once supported people of the
      Early Mississippian Period Macon Plateau culture. From what
      did they build their homes?

Southeast, Puerto Rico and Virgin Islands Region

68   This national memorial pays tribute to a European explorer who reached Florida's Gulf Coast in May 1539, paving the way for others to follow. Name this courageous traveler.

69   With units in Mississippi and Florida, this national seashore is a popular, eventful place. Name this national seashore.

70   What is the national importance of Brices Cross Roads?

71   Ulysses S. Grant received the reputation "Unconditional Surrender Grant" when he forced 13,000 Confederate soldiers at this fort to do just that – surrender. Name the fort where these Confederates surrendered.

72   The Kingsley Plantation, the oldest plantation house in Florida, includes the planter's home, kitchen house and slave quarters. All can be visited at what NPS site?

73   A two-block area of Atlanta honors the life work of what great man and civil rights leader?

74   What was the primary goal of the Shiloh Civil War campaign for both sides?

75   Buck Island Reef National Monument is a magnificent elkhorn coral reef that can be found where?

76   This NPS site protects 18th-19th century Dutch West Indies buildings. Name the national historic site.

77   This is the only known place in America where any member of the Columbus Expedition set foot on US territory. Name this national historic park.

78   When asked by the press where one of his generals was, whom he had not heard from in a month, Lincoln replied, "I know the hole he went into, but I can't tell you for sure what hole he will come out of." To what general were they referring?

Southeast, Puerto Rico and Virgin Islands Region

CHAPTER 6 -
SOUTHEAST, PUERTO RICO AND
VIRGIN ISLANDS REGION
Answers

1   USS Cairo gunboat; Vicksburg National Military Park (NMP), Vicksburg, Mississippi.

2   Cumberland Gap NHP; Kentucky, Tennessee and Virginia.

3   Fort Sumter NM, Charleston harbor, SC.

4   Cape Hatteras NS, Outer Banks, NC. The 4-lighthouses are: Ocracoke Island Light, 1823, 63-ft; Cape Hatteras Light, 1870, 208-ft; Bodie Island Light, 1872, 156-ft; and Currituck Beach Light, 1875, 150-ft.

5   Cape Lookout NS, Outer Banks, North Carolina.

6   Tupelo National Battlefield, Tupelo, Mississippi.

7   Correct answer is B.

8   Mammoth Cave NP, Kentucky.

9   Dry Tortugas NP, 70 miles west of Key West, Florida.
     Sidebar – Floatplanes at Key West carry visitors to and from the park for a reasonable fee. It is an adventurous trip. Expect great views of giant sting-rays, sharks and dolphins because the plane flies low, and the water is crystal clear and shallow.

10   Cumberland Island NS, Georgia.

11   Congaree Swamp NM, South Carolina.

12   Open toad sandals.

13   Everglades NP, Homestead, Florida.

14   Alligator.

15   They get toad away.

16   Marjory Stoneman Douglas, author of <u>The Everglades River of Grass</u>, 1947.

17   Andersonville NHS, Georgia.

18   To visit an ant in Florida.

19   Biscayne NP, Homestead, Florida.

20   Canaveral NS, Titusville, Florida.

21   Jimmy Carter, 39th US President; Jimmy Carter NHS, Plains, Georgia.

22   Andersonville NHS, Georgia.

23   Captain Wirz was tried, convicted of war crimes, and hanged.

24   Virgin Islands NP, St. Johns, Virgin Islands.

25   Two 16th-century Spanish forts; San Felipe del Morro and San Cristobal El Canuelo.
      Sidebar – Both forts contain picturesque architectural features, such as massive masonry walls and corner sentry posts, which appear on auto license plates. Both forts fell to the U.S. Navy during the Spanish-American War of 1898; the forts fired over 400 cannon balls at the American fleet – the U.S. Navy fired fewer than ten, causing the Spanish surrender . . . .result of superior, longer-range cannons.

26   Carl Sandburg NHS, Flat Rock, North Carolina.

27   Carl, it is a red-winged blackbird.

28   Fort Raleigh NHS, Roanoke Island, North Carolina.

29   Sir Walter Raleigh.

30   Col. Thaddeus Kosciuszko from Poland; Star shape; Ninety Six NHS, South Carolina.

31   Sappers.

32   Moores Creek National Battlefield, North Carolina.

33   Cowpens NB, South Carolina.

34   Correct answer is D; Kings Mountain National Military Park, South Carolina.

35   Charles Earl Cornwallis; Guilford Courthouse National Military Park, North Carolina.

36   Granites.

37   Great Smoky NP, North Carolina and Tennessee.

38   Butterflies found at Great Smoky NP.

39   Great Smoky Mountains NP, North Carolina and Tennessee.

40   Everglades NP, Florida.

Southeast, Puerto Rico and Virgin Islands Region

Only U.S. sub-tropical area, these 1,258,670 Florida acres offer exciting bird life, waterways.

41   Correct answer is D; bears will eat corn, but it doesn't grow in the wild.

42   Answers are: **A** = False, bear's den; **B** = True; **C** = True; **D** = True; **E** = True

43   Cans of sardines.
      Sidebar – Cans are put in trees at half-mile intervals and checked every five days for bear signs such as scat, claw-marks or footprints.

44   Bear hunting.
      Sidebar - "Black" Bill killed over 100 bears with his rifle "Old Death" before the NPS banned hunting. Bear hunting is permitted with the proper license at Big South Fork NRRA.

45   Big Cypress N PRES, Ochopee, Florida.

46   Andrew Johnson, 17th U.S. President; Andrew Johnson NHS Greeneville, Tennessee.

47   Spanish troops at St Augustine, Florida.
      Sidebar – It later saw action under the British and American flags.

48   Fort Moultrie, a unit of Fort Sumter NM, Charleston, South Carolina.

49   France.

50   Fort Mantanzas NM St Augustine, Florida.

51   Rifle cannon.

52   Fort Pulaski NM, Savannah, Georgia.

53   Obed WSR, Tennessee.

54   Revolutionary War, 1776.

55   Civil War – Stone Rivers NB, Tennessee.

56   Blue Ridge Parkway.

57   Tuskegee Institute NHS, Alabama.

58   Tuskegee Airmen NHS, Alabama.

59   True.
        Sidebar – "First Americans" are known to have inhabited
        Russell Cave since 7000 BC.

60   Little River Canyon National Preserve, Fort Payne, Alabama.

61   Horseshoe Bend NMP, Dadeville, Alabama.

62   Charles Pinckney NHS, Charleston, North Carolina.

63   Chickamauga and Chattanooga NMP, Georgia and Tennessee.

64   Chattahoochee River NRA, Atlanta, Georgia.

65   Fort Frederica NM, Georgia.

66   Kennesaw Mountain NBP, Atlanta, Georgia.

67   Earthen Mounds.

68   Hernando de Soto; De Soto N MEM, Tampa Bay, Florida.

69   Gulf Islands NS.

70   Civil War National Battlefield Site.

71   Fort Donelson NB, Dover, Tennessee.

72   Timucuan Ecological and Historic Preserve, Jacksonville,
        Florida.

73   Martin Luther King, Jr., NHS.

Southeast, Puerto Rico and
Virgin Islands Region

74   Possession of the railroads; Shiloh NMP, Tennessee.

75   St. Croix, Virgin Islands.

76   Christiansted NHS, St. Croix, Virgin Islands.

77   Salt River Bay NHP and Ecological PRES, VI.

78   General Sherman, during his rampage through Georgia.

Southeast, Puerto Rico and
Virgin Islands Region

CHAPTER 7 –
MIDWEST REGION
Questions and Answers

THE HOMESTEAD ACT

Marking 100th anniversary of Act allowing people to claim 160 acres of unappropriated government land after working it five years.

LOUISIANA PURCHASE

This purchase, negotiated by Livingston and Monroe, secured this area from France for 14 million dollars. Parts of 13 U.S. states apring from it.

The NPS Midwest Region consists of ten states – Ohio, Indiana, Michigan, Wisconsin, Illinois, Missouri, Iowa, Minnesota, Nebraska and Kansas.

CHAPTER 7 –
MIDWEST REGION
Questions

1   On Lake Erie, near Put-in-Bay, the British Navy surrendered to the US Navy. The US Navy Commodore said, "We have met the enemy and they are ours." What is the name of the US Navy Commodore who master-minded the victory and the NPS site that commemorates it?

2   Hardscrabble is not the name of a tougher version of the word-game Scrabble, but the nickname of this president's home . . . he built it himself. Name the president and the NPS site. Hint: His neighbor is Anheuser-Busch.

3   Perhaps the most modern, spacious and environmentally friendly visitor center of all the NPS sites can be found at this national monument, along with lots of teeth, bones and a fine collection of Indian artifacts. It is also one of the most remote national monuments. Name this park.

4   Sometimes called 'A Nebraska Gibraltar,' this milepost for the great wagon train migrations saw 350,000 pioneers pass by from 1841 to 1869. Today it is a national monument. Name the monument.

5   "Bang your oar and chant Viking lore, bang again and chant again", those are the instructions the park rangers shout out, as he and she guide our 20-person canoe away from the marina and into the heart of this out-of-the-ordinary, appealing lake. Water dominates the landscape of this national park, which has 30 glacier-carved lakes. It is a park especially preserved for its scenery and solitude. Name the national park. Hint: Some of the lake names are Rainy, Kabetogama and Sand Point.

6   On or about 1903, this mammal, family and friends swam
        across a lake from the Canadian mainland and settled on this
        island, now a national park. With no predators and lots of food,
        the family grew to a population of about 3,000 by 1948. A
        strange thing happened in 1948; this enormous great lake froze
        and a few other mammals walked across the ice. Now also on
        this island, these new guests reduced the population of the first
        guest to about 1,000 today. Name the national park and its two
        guests.

7   At this national park expect to: watch for moose and hawks,
        listen to loons and wolves, smell the Christmas scent of spruce
        and fir, and admire the rock formations and wildflowers. The
        National Park Service Ranger III and privately owned Queen
        III ferry visitors to and from the park on a 5- to 6-hour journey
        across Lake Superior. This 40-mile long island has no roads
        and no cars, but has 165 miles of hiking trails. It is a serene
        place to get away from civilization. It does have a comfortable
        lodge and housekeeping units, both nestled close to shore,
        where gently rolling waves lap at your balcony, and European
        exchange students serve your meals at a rustic cafeteria.
        The NPS sponsors daily ranger-led boat tours to other islands
        and remote areas of this park; these tours are excellent. Name
        this remote national park.

        Midwest Region

8   If a moose is attacked by a wolf pack what should it do?
        A. Lower its rack of antlers and charge
        B. Stand its ground and wait the wolves out
        C. Run like the wind
        D. Kick with its powerful back hooves

9   Pyramids, domes, obelisks and shrines are archetypal
        memorials to man's noteworthy goals or ambitions or
        achievements. This NPS site incorporates another architectural
        style to memorialize America's lofty goals, soaring ambitions
        and extraordinary achievements. It is home to an inspiring
        museum commemorating the Louisiana Purchase. Its cross-
        section is triangular. Name this nationally important NPS site.
        Hint: It is a monument of elevated, towering and sky-scraping
        beauty.

10   Pioneers outfitted here, steamboats dropped off would-be settlers, the Missouri joins the Mississippi, the Pony Express started its trek west, and mid-19th-century railroads made it this far west. A president sent two explorers west from here. All are good reasons to create this lofty memorial. Name this NPS site.

11   Where did Lewis and Clark begin their expedition, and also winter between December 1803 and May 1804?

12   Assassinated by a crazed job-seeker, Civil War commander of an all-black regiment, this president's home is a national historic site. Name the national historic site.

13   "Uncle Sam is rich enough to give us all a farm."
                    – 1850s popular song.

      This national monument commemorates the heroism of the pioneer settlers. Against improbable odds, they settled the prairie frontier, enticed by the Homestead Act of 1862, which led millions to migrate west, and unscrupulous promoters who claimed the land was fertile and screaming to be cultivated. In reality, as one disheartened sod-buster who gave up said, "it rains grasshoppers, fire and destruction." Name the national monument.

14   Situated near a major metropolitan area, this national lakeshore is an oasis of natural scenic beauty and a recreational paradise, visited each year by tens of thousands. It preserves and protects ever-slowly moving sand dunes, sandy beaches, marine life, bogs, marshes and swamps. Name this national lakeshore.

15   Native American legend has it that a mother bear and her two cubs swam across Lake Michigan. The mother made it, the cubs drowned. She sleeps on the sandy shore waiting for her cubs . . . the cubs, according to myth, turned into two small off-shore islands. Name the national lakeshore and its two islands.

Midwest Region

16   Home to massive sand dunes, dense beech-maple forest and rugged bluffs as high as 460-ft above Lake Michigan, an 1870's lighthouse, a ship-wreck, and a retired life-saving station, this national lakeshore is worth a visit. Name this national lakeshore.

17   "All play and no work makes Jack a mere toy." His Father, 1867. "Never be content until you have done the very best you could have done . . . Work hard in building up the reputation of the family." His Brother, 1869.

Once Governor of the Philippines, this gentleman was raised in the tradition of hard work, fair play and public service, can you already guess who he is? He held the two highest offices in the nation. He opposed Roosevelt's Bull Moose Party. In 1923, he said of himself, "The Court, next to my wife and children, is the nearest thing to my heart in life." Name the national historic site honoring this man. Hint: His father was Secretary of War and Attorney General under President Ulysses S. Grant.

18   Albeit not a national park, this unselfish federation equally qualifies for mention. Loyal to protect an Order, dedicated to preserving a Family, devoted to the individual care of 15 magnificent species of birds, unpretentious in their duty, this non-profit organization manages a most successful wildlife reintroduction program. Relatively unheard of, it maintains a world-class facility to enhance, preserve and protect all of the remaining world cranes population. The facility includes scientific research labs, a dedicated library, breeding areas for all 15 crane species, lecture hall and class rooms, museum, training area for immatures, art gallery, hiking trials and much more. Name this private facility. Hint: It is the only place in the world where all 15 species of cranes can be seen together.

19   Name the two species of cranes that make America their home.

20   About this 2,500 mile-long river President Lincoln said, "It is the backbone of the rebellion (Confederacy) . . . it is the key to the whole situation (Civil War)." Name this national river and recreation area (NRRA). Hint: Samuel Clemens got his nickname here.

Midwest Region

21   Enjoy history and nature in a valley set close to a metropolitan
       area. At this national recreation area you can board a scenic
       railroad and follow a crooked river for a sightseeing excursion
       through the park, rent bicycles, or take a stroll along the Tow
       Path . . . once home to a 19th century canal. Horse-riding,
       hiking, strolling, biking and ski trails are maintained. The park
       is home to Boston Store. Name this national recreation area.
       Hint: Buckeye Trail passes through this NRA.

22   Hopewell Culture National Historical Park in the Ohio Valley
       consists of mounds and earthworks built by whom?

23   "What dreams we have
              and how they fly."

       An African-American poet, who wrote the verse above and
       authored twenty-one books during his short life span, this
       acclaimed writer rose from a poor childhood in Dayton, Ohio
       to befriend such famous Americans as Frederick Douglas and
       Booker T. Washington. What is his name? His home is now a
       unit of what national historical park?

24   At Dayton Aviation Heritage National Historical Park, Wilbur
       and Orville Wright ran a mechanical manufacture and repair
       business. What did they manufacture?

25   At this unit of Dayton Aviation Heritage NHP, Wilbur and
       Orville Wright flew and tested their experimental airplanes and
       conducted a flying school. Name this unit of Dayton Aviation
       Heritage NHP.

26   East Channel Lighthouse, Indian Head, Rainbow Cave, Lovers'
       Leap, Miners Castle, boat cruises, swimming, beach-combing,
       hiking and camping are some of the neat things to see and do at
       this national lakeshore. Name this national lakeshore.

27   Lake Superior scenic archipelago islands, 22 strong, comprise
       this national lakeshore, which is home to 150 species of nesting
       birds. Light stations, and their need for firewood, inadvertently
       set aside wood reserves that went unclaimed and today are old-

Midwest Region

growth hardwood forests. Together, the light stations and old-growth forests "up the ante" of interest in this vacation mecca. Name this archipelago.

28   Biologists worked for decades to rid Lake Superior of a parasite that was sucking the life out of the lake trout fisheries. They successfully controlled the parasite and restored commercial and recreational fishing. What was the terrible parasite?

29   He believed that the best defense was a good offense – no, he wasn't a football player – and he put this strategy to good use in helping to defeat the British and Indians. During the Revolutionary War he outfoxed the British and forced them to surrender Fort Sackville, Vincennes, Indiana.
      What national historical park honors this accomplished warrior and bears his name?

30   Early 19th-century farming was the way of life for this boy, who would later grow up to be president. His mother died when he was age 11 of "milksick" poison, which occurs when a cow eats the snake-root plant and people drink its tainted milk. Name this national memorial.

31   Nicodemus National Historic Site preserves a small town in Kansas that was established in 1877 by a group of southern Americans. The town is dedicated to the perseverance of what group of people?

32   The landmark Supreme Court case that ended racial segregation in public schools is commemorated at this national historic site. Name the national historic site.

33   Established in 1996 to preserve a small segment of our tallgrass prairie ecosystem that once covered a good part of North America, this site includes native American artifacts and historic structures from the Z Bar/Spring Hill Ranch. Name this park.

Midwest Region

34   Fort Scott was established to keep the peace on the prairie during the Indian Wars, "Bleeding Kansas" and Civil War periods. It has been restored to its 1840's appearance. Twenty buildings and 33 historically furnished rooms are on exhibit. Five acres of _____ are also protected. Name the missing ingredient.

35   "I liked Indians . . . . She was handsome, her countenance showed that discipline of life which he admired . . . (It's an) Indian way to pass through a country without disturbing anything; to pass and leave no trace, like fish through water, or birds through the air. . . . men travel faster now, but I do not know if they go to better places."
Death Comes for the Archbishop, Willa Cather.

Willa's fine novel about the French explorer-clergy who "liked Indians" in 17th-18th century North America accurately portrays the life of what honorable French priest and explorer?

Midwest Region

36   This Indian Wars-era fort is one of the best preserved, with nine original buildings dating back to 1866. It has a 44-acre virgin prairie site adjacent to the Pawnee River. Name this national historic site.

37   One hundred and ninety prehistoric burial and ceremonial mounds are found at this national monument. Name the national monument.

38   The 31st president of the United States lived here. Whose house is it?

39   George Washington Carver National Monument is the birthplace and home of Carver, who ascended from slavery to prominence as an educator and humanitarian. In what other area did Carter contribute to the well-being of man?

40   This National Historic Site bestows honor on our country's 33rd President. The park consists of five properties and a collection of memorabilia linked with the life of the president

and his family. You may visit the President's House, Frank Wallace House, George Wallace House, Noland House and President's Farm. Name the President.

41   Designated in 1964, these scenic riverways include the Current and Jacks Fork Rivers – the first rivers to receive national protection. Name the scenic riverways.

42   Wilson's Creek National Battlefield commemorates a battle fought during what war?

43   Named by *National Geographic Traveler* as one of America's top outdoor adventures, this national scenic river is a canoeist's delight. It winds through sand-hills, boreal and eastern woodland, Rocky Mountain forest and tallgrass prairie. Name this national scenic river.

44   Saint Croix National Scenic Riverway includes within its protective boundary the Saint Croix River and what other prominent river?

45   A Native America quarry for hundreds of years, great craftsmen have carved ceremonial and traditional pipes from the soft, red clay found at this NPS site. Name this quarry.

46   Just below the Canadian border, this national monument is located near the headwaters of the Mississippi River. Fur trappers hand-carried their canoes and goods over a 10-mile pass to avoid a nasty waterfall at this NPS site. Guess the national monument.

47   Keweenaw National Historic Park preserves the history of a century's mining operation. Pure masses of what ore were extracted from the Keweenaw mines?

48   This historic site features a museum with exhibits about the first ladies. Ida McKinley once lived here. Name this national historic site.

Midwest Region

49   The Battle of Fallen Timbers led to defeat of the British by
      General "Mad" Anthony Wayne and resulted in what treaty?

50   "As the cone scatters the seeds of the pine and fir tree,
                  so may it scatter the seeds of wisdom and understanding
                  among men, to the end that every citizen may learn to hold
                  the lives of harmless wild creatures as a public trust for
                  human good, against the abuse of which he stands personally
                  responsible." *Pine Cone,* Guess the author.

      The author of the above was a self-taught ecologist, soil
      scientist and range manager. He wrote a handbook on game and
      fish management, and several books including Sand County
      Almanac, and Round River.He maintained an experimental
      farm in Wisconsin. Name this talented naturalist.

Midwest Region

CHAPTER 7 –
MIDWEST REGION
Answers

1   Commodore Perry; Perry's Victory and International Peace Memorial

2   President Ulysses S. Grant; Ulysses S. Grant NHS, St. Louis, Missouri.
Sidebar – Anheuser-Busch bought the farmland once plowed by President Grant and made it home to more than 1,000 animals from six continents. Known today as 'Grant's Farm', it is a great place to visit, and is home to the famous Anheuser-Busch Clydesdale Stables.

3   Agate Fossil Beds NM, Nebraska.

4   Scotts Bluff NM, Nebraska.

5   Voyageurs NP, International Falls, Minnesota.
Sidebar – Before setting out, park rangers teach you the Viking mantra/chant and how to paddle the canoe. Yes, everyone must paddle and pull your own weight. Reservations for the ranger-led canoe, day-outing are required; call (218) 283-9821.

6   Isle Royale NP, Michigan: moose and gray wolves.

7   Isle Royale NP, Michigan.

8   Correct answer is B.

9   Jefferson National Expansion Memorial and Gateway Arch, St. Louis, Missouri.

Midwest Region

10   Jefferson National Expansion Memorial and Gateway Arch, St. Louis, Missouri. Sidebar – The 630-feet high Gateway Arch, an enormous engineering feat, was constructed in 1965. A tram carries a few people at a time to the top, where an observation room awaits the courageous visitor. From its low windows, (be prepared to lay on your belly and squirm-like-a-worm), viewers are treated to spectacular vistas of the Mighty Mississippi and its many river-boats, and a majestic view of the beautiful modern city of Saint Louis. Below the Arch is located the Museum of Westward Expansion, which is well worth a visit. It houses a bronze statue of Thomas Jefferson, Lewis and Clark's expedition journal, and field sketches of flora and fauna, expedition Indian artifacts, paintings depicting St. Louis in its 19th-century heyday, and stuffed animals such as long-horn steer, appaloosa horse, pronghorn antelope and grizzly bear.

11   Camp Wood.

12   James A. Garfield NHS; 20th U.S. President.
        Sidebar – Garfield was president for less than a year, shot soon after his inauguration in 1881. Garfield did not die from the gun shot, *per se*, but died six months later of lead poisoning, because a botched operation failed to remove the bullet.

13   Homestead National Monument of America, Nebraska.

14   Indiana Dunes National Lakeshore, Porter, Indiana.

15   Sleeping Bear Dunes NL, Empire, Michigan; North and South Manitou Island.

16   Sleeping Bear Dunes NL, Empire, Michigan.

17   William Howard Taft NHS, Cincinnati, Ohio.

18   The International Crane Federation – ICF, Baraboo, Wisconsin.

19   Whooping crane and sandhill crane.

Midwest Region

20   Mississippi NRRA, Minnesota to Gulf of Mexico; While
        guiding riverboats and checking shallow water level, Clemens
        would shout, "mark four, mark three, MARK TWAIN . . . "

21   Cuyahoga Valley NRA, Cleveland, Ohio.
        Sidebar – Remnants of the Ohio and Erie Canal pass through
        the park. Boston Store has an interesting exhibit on canal-boat
        building.

22   A "lost race" of native Americans who lived between 2,200 and
        1,500 years ago. The earthworks were burial mounds to
        memorialize their dead.

23   Paul Lawrence Dunbar; Dayton Aviation Heritage National
        Historical Park, Ohio.

24   Bicycles and printing machines.

25   Huffman Prairie Flying Field; Wright-Patterson Air Force Base,
        Ohio – Enter the Airbase at Gate 12A and request a visitor
        pass.
        Sidebar – Albeit not a NPS site, the United States Air Force
        Museum, located adjacent to Wright-Patterson Air Force Base,
        has the finest collection of full-sized aircraft in the world on
        display, and is four times as large as the National Air and Space
        Museum in WDC. Countries from all over the world have
        donated aircraft. Its IMAX theatre offers great shows with
        something for the entire family.

26   Pictured Rocks NL Lake Superior, Michigan.

27   Apostle Islands NL, Wisconsin

28   Sea lamprey.

29   George Rogers Clark NHP, Vincennes, Indiana.

30   Lincoln Boyhood N MEM Lincoln City, Indiana.

31   African Americans.

Midwest Region

32   Brown *v.* Board of Education NHS, Topeka, Kansas.

33   Tallgrass Prairie N PRES Cottonwood Falls, Kansas.

34   Tallgrass Prairie.

35   Father Marquette N MEM, Straits of Mackinac, Michigan.

36   Fort Larned NHS, Larned, Kansas.

37   Effigy Mounds NM, Marquette, Iowa.

38   Herbert Hoover.

39   Science.
      Sidebar – He invented alternative uses for soybeans, including
      synthetic tires. His studies led to a scientific system for rotating
      crops to restore nutrients in soil.

40   Harry S Truman.

41   Ozark NSR, Van Buren, Missouri.

42   Civil War.

43   Niobrara NSR, O'Neill, Nebraska.

44   Namekagon River.

45   Pipestone NM, Minnesota.

46   Grand Portage NM, Grand Marais, Minnesota.

47   Copper.

48   First Ladies NHS, Canton, Ohio.

49   Treaty of Greeneville – Learn more about it at Fallen Timbers
      Battlefield and Fort Miamis NHS, Toledo, Ohio.

50   Aldo Leopold.

CHAPTER 8 –
SOUTHWEST REGION
Questions and Answers

Relations with our neighbors . . .

Relationships with each other . . .

Relationships with the land . . .

The NPS Southwest Region consists of five states: Texas, Oklahoma, New Mexico, Arkansas and Louisiana.

CHAPTER 8 –
SOUTHWEST REGION
Questions

1   The Rio Grande River gracefully bends through what national parks?

2   Where does the Rio Grande River begin and end?

3   This site housed the first military post and federal court in the Louisiana Territory and was home to the notorious Judge Parker – 'The Hanging Judge'. Name the site.

4   This national memorial commemorates the first European settlement of the Lower Mississippi Valley. It was established in 1686 and served as a fort during both the Revolution and the Civil War. Name the monument.

5   This historic site commemorates the "Little Rock Nine" and symbolizes the federal government's commitment to eliminate racial segregation in schools. Name the national historic site.

6   Born to blend in, this little creature is hard to spot. It is perfectly adapted to match its reddish sandstone habitat. It can be found at Big Bend National Park. What is it?

7   This national park is home to the Mexican free-tailed bat, which puts on an evening show from early in May through October. Name this national park.

8   Ancient fossil reef remnants, high above sea level, can be explored at this national park. Name the park.

9   Soldiers from this fort protected settlers from Comanche and Apache raids along the infamous El Paso to San Antonio Road between 1854 and 1891. Now a national historic site; name the fort.

10   "The light is psychedelic, the dry electric air
         narcotic. To me the desert . . . sharpens and
         heightens vision, touch, hearing, taste, and
         smell. Each stone, each plant, each grain of
         sand exists in and for itself with a clarity that
         is undimmed by any suggestion of a different realm."
                     Edward Abbey, <u>Desert Solitude</u>

I am the largest gypsum dune field in the world. Who am I?

11   Carved into the sides of a volcanic escarpment some 12,000
     years ago are thousands of symbols reflecting the trials and
     tribulations of Indian life. Name the national monument that
     protects this art.

12   This cinder-cone volcano erupted between 56 and 62,000 years
     ago. It is a beautiful, peaceful park to visit. You may drive your
     car along a spiral route to the top of the cinder cone, 1,200 feet
     high. You'll pass beside a pinon-juniper woodland biotic
     community on the way. Name this national monument.
     Hint: Its name is Spanish for chokecherry.

13   Known for its inscriptions in rock, some made by European
     explorers, but most made from AD 1100 to AD 1400 by native
     Americans, this monument is a massive sandstone mesa rising
     200 feet from the plains below. Name this national monument.

14   Accessible by a steep 180-ft. climb along an unpaved self-
     guided hike, these ruins are one of the finest in the NPS
     system. Built in the late 13th century by the Mogollon people,
     these cliff dwellings look today very much as they did when
     they were inhabited. Name this national monument. Hint:
     Name a reptile with orange, black and yellow scales.

15   Site of one of the longest lava tubes in North America.
     Sandstone bluffs and mesas with sprawling forests of pine and
     aspen are common. Home to the Candelaria Ice Cave, which
     contains permanent ice all year – name this peculiar national
     monument. Hint: Monuments name means 'the bad country'.

Southwest Region

16   A prehistoric ancestral home of Pueblo people, this national historic park is in a remote location, with access only by dirt roads that are sometimes impassable in wet conditions. Best known for its complex architectural-engineering feat of building adobe shelters on the flat canyon floor, this site also contains a few small cliff dwellings and many archaeological sites. Name the national historic park.

17   Swamp, marshland, upland, battlefield, cemetery, and classy quarter – your land and my land – are on exhibition to illustrate natural, cultural and historic significance at this national historic park and preserve.
      Name this national historic park and preserve. Hint: Visit all six units.

18   Pearl Harbor forever changed the way our military protects us, Timothy McVeigh forever changed the way our government protects itself. This NPS site is a memorial to 168 people killed in the deadliest terror attack known, at the time, on U.S. soil. Name the site that commemorates this tragic event in American history.

19   Cotton kingdom and southern antebellum properties are on display at this national historic park. Tour an 18th-century fortification built by the French and occupied by the Spanish and British. Where am I?

20   A free black man owned a home and business that is open for view at Natchez National Historic Park, Mississippi. He left his diary for us to peruse and enjoy the heart-rending tales of everyday life in old-time Natchez. Who was this free man, author and gentleman?

21   This battlefield commemorates the 1862 Civil War battle that established Union control of Missouri. A portion of the Cherokee Trail of Tears also goes through the park. Name this national military park.

22   Therapeutic baths have treated rheumatism, polio and other related ailments for over 200 years at this national park site. Name this national park. Hint: Presidents have been treated here.

23   Floating this wild river gives one the feeling you've gone back 100 years in time. Mountain splendor pales in comparison with twists and turns, sink-holes and springs, waterfalls and rock formations that dominate this national river. Authorized by Congress in 1972, it was the first river to receive national recognition. Name it!

24   European settlement to the lower Mississippi Valley was first credited to Arkansas Post in 1686. Name the gentleman responsible.

25   Long-horn steer, remnants of oil drill rigs and other country paraphernalia are on display at this past president's ranch. Name the presidential national historic park.

26   People quarried flint for tools here for 12,000 years, beginning with the Clovis Ice Age tribe. Name this national monument.

27   Aptly named, Big Thicket protects four prominent ecosystems that converge at the park, which includes nine land units and four water units. Two of the ecosystems are western arid desert and eastern hardwood forest; name the two other ecosystems.

28   Chamizal National Memorial commemorates the peaceful settlement of a dispute between the United States and Mexico, which resulted in the Chamizal Treaty of 1963. What was the dispute about?

29   What was the main purpose of Fort Davis NHS?

30   This recreation area on the Canadian River attracts 1.5 million visitors a year. Name it!

31   This national seashore enjoys unique status as the longest barrier island, at 70 miles, in the world. Name it!

Southwest Region

32   This battlefield commemorates the Mexican-American War of 1846-48, in which Mexico ceded claims to Texas, New Mexico, Arizona, Utah, Nevada and California to the United States. Name this national historic site.

33   Still used as Catholic churches today, thus forming an unbroken link with the past, these 18th-century Spanish missions – Concepcion, San Jose, San Juan and Espada – form what national historic park?

34   West Ruin, a pueblo of 400 ruins that is open to the public, was last inhabited by the Anasazi during the 12th and 13th centuries. What is the name of this national monument?

35   Civil War battles at Glorieta Pass, a former cattle ranch and 15th-century pueblo ruins, are all ghosts from the past, but open to modern day exploration at what national historic park?

36   Abo, Quarai and Gran Quivira are the three principal stone ruins to visit at what national monument?

37   How many forts occupied the site now known as Fort Union National Monument?

38   Two plantations – Magnolia and Oakland – dating back to 1820, are on exhibit at what national Historic Park?

39   Poverty Point National Monument preserves and protects what national treasure?

40   The origin and progression of modern jazz are interpreted for you at what national historic park?

41   Who fought at the Washita Battlefield National Historic Site, Cheyenne, Oklahoma?

42   Camping, boating, fishing, hiking, swimming, hunting and just plain-vanilla enjoying the great outdoors is done everyday at this national recreation area in Oklahoma. Name this national recreation area.

43   Where did Davy Crockett and Daniel Boone die?

CHAPTER 8 –
SOUTHWEST REGION
Answers

1   Rio Grande Wild and Scenic River (W and SR), Big Bend NP and Amistad Recreation Area (RA)

2   The Rio Grande River begins in the Rocky Mountains and ends up mingling with Mississippi River mud in the great Gulf of Mexico.

3   Fort Smith NHS, Fort Smith, Arkansas.

4   Arkansas Post NM.

5   Little Rock Central High School NHS.

6   Texas horned lizard.

7   Carlsbad Caverns NP, New Mexico.

8   Guadalupe Mountains NP, Pipe Springs, Texas.

9   Fort Davis NHS, Texas.

10   White Sands NM, Las Cruces, New Mexico.

11   Petroglyph NM, Albuquerque, New Mexico.

12   Capulin Volcano NM, Capulin, New Mexico.

13   El Moro NM, Grants, New Mexico.

14   Gila Cliff Dwellings NM, Silver City, New Mexico.

15   El Malpais NM, Grants, New Mexico.

Southwest Region

16   Chaco Culture NHP, Bloomfield, New Mexico.

17   Jean Lafitte NHP and PRES New Orleans, Louisiana.

18   Oklahoma City NM.
        Sidebar – NPS memorial was built on the former site of the
        Alfred P. Murrah Federal Building, which was destroyed in the
        blast on April 19, 1995.

19   Natchez NHP, Mississippi.

20   William Johnson.

21   Pea Ridge NMP, Arkansas.

22   Hot Springs NP, Arkansas.

23   Buffalo NR, Harrison, Arkansas.

24   Henri de Tonti - Arkansas Post N MEM, Gillett, Arkansas.

25   Lyndon B. Johnson NHP – 36th US President; Johnson City,
        Texas.

26   Alibates Flint Quarry NM, Amarillo, Texas.

27   Western Prairie and Southern Coastal Wetland.

28   Boundary dispute.

29   To protect setters from Apaches and Comanches.

30   Lake Meredith NRA, Amarillo, Texas.

31   Padre Island NS.

32   Palo Alto Battlefield NHS, Brownsville, Texas.

33   San Antonio Missions NHP, San Antonio, Texas.

Southwest Region

34   Aztec Ruins NM, Aztec, New Mexico.

35   Pecos NHP, Pecos, New Mexico.

36   Salinas Pueblo NM, Mountainair, New Mexico

37   Three.

38   Cane River NHP Natchitoches, Louisiana.

39   Prehistoric earthworks.

40   New Orleans Jazz NHP, Louisiana.

41   Plains Indians and the US Army; Cheyenne, Oklahoma.

42   Chickasaw NRA, Oklahoma.

43   At the Alamo, San Antonio, Texas. (Not a NPS site.)

Southwest Region

CHAPTER 9 –
ROCKY MOUNTAIN REGION
Questions and Answers

Monument in Black Hills of Wyoming, established by Theodore Roosevelt, consists of 865 vertical ft. of rock romation.

Into this mountain were carved the heads of Washington, Jefferson, Lincoln and T. Roosevelt.

Commemorating the joining of the tracks of the Union Pacific and Central Pacific Railroads (1869) in a dramatic ceremony at Promontory, Utah.

Rocky Mountain Region

The NPS Rocky Mountain Region consists of six states – Utah, Colorado, Wyoming, Montana, North and South Dakota.

CHAPTER 9 –
ROCKY MOUNTAIN REGION
Questions

"A thing of beauty is a joy forever." John Keats

1   Colorful, yellow wildflowers flourish on sage flats at Jackson Lake Grand Tetons NP, Wyoming. These daisies are named after what part of an animal?
    A.   Doe fur
    B.   Elk horn
    C.   Moose hoof
    D.   Mule ear

2   At this national park, visitors can ride a tram to the top of Rendezvous Mountain and then hike downhill through flower-filled meadows with spectacular views. Name the park.

3   What president's faces did sculptor Gutzon Borglum carve into the granite mountain at Mount Rushmore NM Keystone, South Dakota? Should we carve any others?

4   To reach the peak of this rocky mountain you must climb to 14,160 feet above sea level, pass through a keyhole and navigate over a rugged boulder field. What peak and national park is this?

5   This road connects the east and west entrances to Rocky Mountain NP and happens to be the highest paved highway in America. Name the recognized road.

6   Who managed Yellowstone NP from 1876 until the National
        Park Service was formed in 1916?

7   "It is not the strongest of the species that survive,
                Nor the most intelligent,
                But the one most responsive to change."
                        Charles Darwin, Origin of Species

        What is the most abundant large mammal at Yellowstone?

8   What is the Native American name for elk?

9   Name the world's most famous geyser and where it is?

10   Bison and pronghorn antelope graze here. In the fall, elk
        bugling can be heard. Mule deer browse close enough to the
        roads to be seen by visitors. All these animals pound the roof-
        top of the caves below. You will not go home without seeing a
        herd of buffalo. Name this national park.

11   Colorado's highest cliff, Painted Wall, rises 2,240 feet above
        the river floor at this national monument. Name the national
        monument. The monument is home to black bear, mule deer,
        golden eagle and peregrine falcon.

12   Irregular shaped pillars of colorful rock, weathered away by
        wind and rain, form fantasy characters ready to perform on
        nature's stage at the amphitheater in this national park. Erosion
        has carved limestone, sandstone and mudstone into mazes of

Rocky Mountain Region

pink pinnacles and spires. Known to the native Americans as Hoodoos, rock-forms take on the shapes of wizards and goblins, princes and princesses, kings and queens, and your cherished dreams and nasty nightmares. Name the national park.

13 Oak Tree House and Square Tower House cliff dwellings are only two of 23 prehistoric Indian dwellings at this national park. Name the national park. Hint: What has four corners?

14 Named after my favorite tree, this national monument also houses colorful Hoodoos. Name the monument. Hint: Although neighboring, it is smaller than Bryce and closed by heavy snow in the winter.

15 Virgin River Narrows – a deep–slot canyon with 2,000-ft walls, tapering to 30-ft in width – Checkerboard Mesa – a sandstone mountain with a vertical and horizontal pattern of surface cracks resembling a play board – and Kolob Arch – the world's longest single-span natural rock arch, with a span of 310-feet – can be viewed at this sublime national park. Be sure not to miss Weeping Rock, its Emerald Pools and the Great White Throne. Name the national park?

16 This site commemorates the completion of the nation's first transcontinental railroad from east coast to west coast, approximately 3,000 miles. On May 10, 1869, representatives of the Union Pacific and Central Pacific railroads met at Promontory, Utah, and drove the ceremonial last spike connecting both lines. On hand for the celebration that day in 1869 were two locomotives – the '119' and the 'Jupiter'. Today, a replica steam locomotive is on exhibition . . . go between April and mid-October to see it operate. Name the national historic site.

17 As glaciers retreated over 12,000 years ago, they scoured the land and spread sand and gravel across the San Luis Valley. Winds over eons swept the sand into piles, some 750-feet high, creating the tallest sand dunes in North America – and this national monument. Name the national monument.

18 Strong winds that blow from every direction create what type of sand dune?

19 Choose which item below is **not** a sand dune pattern:
    A = Star dune   B = Transverse dune
    C = Crescent dune   D = Bandanna dune
                E = U-shaped dune

20 Fringed-toed lizards, darkling beetles, multi-legged caterpillars, purple verbena, squaw-bush and other brilliant wildflowers are life forms you expect to find in what biotic community?
    A = Swamps   B = Oak woodlands
    C = Sand dunes   D = Savannas

21 Striped and rocky landscapes, fins, thin walls of rocks, windows, arches, arches and more arches are my trade-mark. Name this national park.

22 Located at the intersection of the Colorado and Green Rivers, this national park is home to Horse Hoof Arch, perhaps the most beautiful arch in the world. Name this national park.

23 Sinuous wrinkles in the Earth's crust, caused 65 million years ago, make travel across this national park limited and difficult, but the colorful cliffs, domes and monoliths make it worth the effort. The site also protects the historic Fremont culture, remains of a Mormon settlement. Name the national park.

24 Home to the world's largest natural bridge (a bridge crosses water, an arch does not) this national park is considered sacred by native Americans. Name the national monument.

25 Owachomo, Sipapu and Kachina represent three phases in the development and climax of this geological feature. Name the national monument for which the feature is known. Hint: The site also contains Puebloan archaeological sites.

Rocky Mountain Region

26   High on a bluff in 1525, an agricultural society of Hidatsa Indians tended their gardens of beans, corn, tobacco, sunflowers, pumpkins and squash. They lived in the village of Awatixa Xi'e and expanded to another village called Hidatsa in 1600. They merged with Mandan Indians and formed a third village called Awatixa in 1796. The villages are now preserved as a national historic site . . . name the site.

27   Stegosaurus stenops is a plant-eating dinosaur with plates running down both sides of its back. A 30-feet long, life-sized model of one is on display at this national monument visitor center. Also at the VC is a gallery of some 1,500 dinosaur bones exposed in a rock wall. Name the national monument.

28   What type of forest was buried 35 million years ago at Florissant Fossil Beds National Monument?

29   Mostly in Utah, this national recreation area embraces the second largest man-made lake in America. Beautiful orange and red sandstone canyons, fishing, house-boating, and its sparkling blue waters attract visitors from all over the world. Name this national recreation area.

30   Albeit not a NPS site, this Utah State Park is worth honorable mention. Its unique coral-colored sand dunes are stunning. Dunes support attractive clusters of long-leafed sunflowers and Welch's milkweed – a plant that grows only here. Name this Utah State Park.

31   Taking refuge on the high plains at the crossroads of Mexico and America, two brothers set up a trading post in 1829. They became so successful trading between the Plains Indians and the Mexicans that the U.S. Government considered them "peacemakers" and set up an Indian Agency at the post. Name this national historic site.

32   "Owl Woman" was the wife of what well known Indian Trader? Hint: He became the first Governor of New Mexico and was killed during a Pueblo Indian and New Mexican insurrection.

Rocky Mountain Region

33   "It sailed over Nick's shoulder and onto the bank behind him.
      Nick saw him shine in the sun and then he found him where he
      was tumbling in the ferns. He was strong and heavy in Nick's
      hands and he had a pleasant smell and Nick saw how dark his
      back was and how brilliant his spots were colored and how
      bright the edges of his . . . They were white on the edge with a
      black line behind and then there was the lovely golden sunset
      color of his belly."
                          <u>Nick Adams Stories</u>, Ernest Hemingway

      What was it Nick held in his hands?

34   Why did no one fish off Noah's Ark?

35   Donating tons of money, time and talent, this humanitarian,
      philanthropist and national park promoter specifically
      contributed to the development of Acadia, Grand Teton, Great
      Smoky Mountain and Virgin Islands national parks. His name
      appears on the NPS land that "connects and protects" the
      ecosystem between Grand Teton and Yellowstone national
      parks. What is his name?

36   The nation's first national monument, proclaimed in 1906 by
      President Teddy Roosevelt, this tower is sacred to the Plains
      Indian tribes. It rises 867 feet from a pine- forest floor and is a
      haven for rock climbers. Name this national monument.

37   This fort was built at the confluence of the North Platte and
      Laramie rivers in 1834, and served Indians, trappers, traders,
      pioneers, soldiers and Pony Express riders, each in their turn,
      for over 50 years. Name this national historic site. Hint: It bears
      the name of its surroundings.

38   It contains the largest mixed-grass prairie in the country, is rich
      in Oligocene era mammal fossils, and is known for its
      outstanding geological features. Steep canyons and rough
      terrain make for fun back-packing. Name this national park.

39   With over 110 miles underground already surveyed, this
      national monument is the third longest cave in the world. Name
      this national monument.

Rocky Mountain Region

40   The fossilized fish, plants, birds, insects and mammals of this
      fresh-water lake date back to a period 50 million years ago.
      Name this national monument.

41   American Fur Company built this trading post in 1828 along
      the Missouri River to trade for beaver fur and buffalo robes.
      Name this national historic site.

42   Nestled in the colorful North Dakota Badlands, Theodore
      Roosevelt National Park offers opportunities to view what
      exciting wildlife? (Choose most correct answer.)
      A. buffalo and elk;
      B. buffalo, elk and wild horses;
      C. buffalo, elk, wild horses and pronghorn;
      D. buffalo, elk, wild horses, pronghorn and prairie dogs

43   Dynamic in character, this national recreation river winds and
      bends, snags and drags, past many chutes, sand bars and
      islands. It flows between Nebraska and South Dakota, adjacent
      to plain forest, tallgrass and mixed-grass prairie. Name this
      national recreation river.

44   This site commemorates the 150-plus years of peace between
      the United States and Canada. Formal gardens are superb,
      delicate and exquisite. Name the park.

45   Name two ranches begun by Teddy Roosevelt in North Dakota.

46   Two Air Force officers sat 24 hours, 7 days a week, all year
        long, inside a capsule, just in case they would someday be
        needed to launch a nuclear war. That cold war threat is not as
        dire as it once was; consequently, America is scaling back its
        nuclear arsenal. That underground capsule and missile silo can
        be viewed at what national historic site?

47   Three reservoirs provide great boating and fishing on the
        Gunnison River of south-central Colorado. High-wall canyons
        make for interesting climbs and hikes. Name this national
        recreation area.

48   Red monoliths, sheer-walled canyons, a whiff of mountain air,
        isolation, cacophony echoes and prehistoric Indian culture
        combine their character to form this colorful sandstone country
        national monument.
        Name this out-of-the-way, hard-to-get-to, national monument.

49   "It is a magnificent job, perfectly accomplished.
                Workmen who risked their lives daily on the face
                of the steep cliffs, that had to be conquered to make
                this modern trail, deserve special honor for their
                share in its undertaking."
                        Harold Ickes, Secretary of the Interior, 1934

        In 1933, the National Park Service wanted to build a
        spectacular road to heights and daring never tried before, and
        they wanted to do it without the use of power shovels. "No
        derricks . . . they make too much noise and smoke", cried the
        park service; "No road", cried the contractors, "We can't build
        without them". Nevertheless, Going-To-The-Sun Road got
        built, you be the judge how. Name the national park where you
        can drive it.

50   This national park shares a common border with a Canadian
        national park and now goes by the joint name. What is it now
        called?

Rocky Mountain Region

51   Unbeknownst to the Nez Perce, just before dawn U.S. Cavalry stealthily strung out along the slope where the Indians' horse herd was grazing. On the morning of August 9, 1877, the Cavalry charged into the Nez Perce's camp and began clubbing any Indian that went by . . . they clubbed men, women and children, some of them in their sleep. Bloody hand-to-hand combat ensued . . . before it was over 60 Indians and 40 soldiers were killed. What is the name of this national battlefield?

52   Which name below was **not** a Nez Perce Chief?
A.   Joseph
B.   Iron Horse
C.   Looking Glass
D.   Poker Joe

53   Where does Bighorn Canyon National Recreation Area derive its name?

54   A Canadian fur trader and a cattle baron joined fortunes to form a 19th-century range ranch, now a national historic site in Montana. Name it.

55   There is only one place in America where four states come together . . . what state is not a member of the famous four-corners area?
A.   Nevada
B.   Utah
C.   Arizona
D.   New Mexico

56   In the southwest corner of Colorado, near Cortez, there survives beautiful ancient stone architecture from 500 BC. What is this incredible national monument?

57   This national monument is a cave site in Utah. Name it!

CHAPTER 9 –
ROCKY MOUNTAIN REGION
Answers

1   Correct answer is D – mule ear daisies.

2   Grand Teton NP. Wyoming.

3   Presidents Washington, Jefferson, Lincoln and Teddy
Roosevelt.

4   Long's Peak; Rocky Mountain National Park, Estes Park,
Colorado.

5   Trail Ridge road . . . its highest point is 12,183-feet above sea
level.

6   No one from 1876 to 1886 . . . US Army Calvary from 1886 to
1916.
Sidebar – The army was called in to control the illegal
poaching and timber-logging practices. The army spent most of
its time chasing poachers and illegal lumber thieves. They built
Historic Fort Yellowstone – headquarters and barracks – at
Mammoth Hot Springs, the northern entrance to the park. The
buildings are still used today as a NPS administrative office,
visitor center, cafeteria and museum.

7   Elk.
Sidebar – Without natural predation, elk herds have swelled and
been forced to search elsewhere for food. They pushed south
out of the park and into Jackson Hole, Wyoming, where the
government has built large enclosures to contain them. Some of
them have been relocated to other parks in California and
Oregon. Now that wolves have been reintroduced in
Yellowstone, it is hoped nature will take its course and keep the
elk population in check.

Rocky Mountain Region

8   Wapiti.

9   Old Faithful; Old Faithful Village, Yellowstone NP, Wyoming side.

10   Wind Cave NP, South Dakota.

11   Black Canyon of the Gunnison NP, East of Montrose, Colorado.
    Sidebar – The 'Painted Wall' effect was created 30 million years ago, when dark metamorphic rock began to crack and allowed light-colored molten lava to seep into the cracks, forming horizontal bands.

12   Bryce Canyon NP Tropic, Arizona.

13   Mesa Verde NP Cortez, Colorado.

14   Cedar Breaks NM Cedar City, Utah.

15   Zion NP, Springdale, Arizona.

16   Golden Spike NHS Promontory, Utah.

17   Great Sand Dunes NM, Alamosa, Colorado.

18   Star dune.

19   Correct answer is D.

20   Correct answer is C.

21   Arches NP, Moab, Utah.

22   Canyonlands NP, Moab, Utah.

23   Capitol Reef NP, Torrey, Utah.

24   Rainbow Bridge NM, Lake Power, Utah.

Rocky Mountain Region

25   Natural Bridges NM, Blanding, Utah.

26   Knife River Indian Villages NHS, Stanton, North Dakota.

27   Dinosaur National Monument, Dinosaur, Colorado.
Sidebar – Park provides two self-guided auto tours: Tour of the Tilted Rocks, and Journey Through Time. Green and Yampa River Canyons are spectacular.

28   Redwood forest; Florissant Fossil Beds National Monument, Colorado Springs, Colorado

29   Glen Canyon NRA, Page, Arizona.

30   Coral Pink Sand Dunes State Park, Kanab, Utah.

31   Bent's Old Fort NHS, Colorado.

32   Charles Bent, of Bent's Old Fort NHS, Colorado, was married to a Cheyenne Indian and often lived with her tribe, where he was known as "Little White Man".

33   Rainbow Trout.
Sidebar – Some NPs, such as Yellowstone, Rocky Mountain and Grand Teton, will allow fly fishing – no bait, and catch and release is often required. You must have a legitimate State fishing license. Each visitor center has information on special park fishing regulations, bait restrictions, creel limits and open season.

34   They had only two worms.

35   John D. Rockefeller, Jr., Memorial Parkway

36   Devils Tower NM, Wyoming.

37   Fort Laramie NHS, Wyoming.

38   Badlands NP, South Dakota.

Rocky Mountain Region

39   Jewel Cave NM, Custer, South Dakota.

40   Fossil Butte NM, Kemmerer, Wyoming.

41   Fort Union Trading Post NHS Williston, North Dakota.

42   Most correct answer is D.

43   Missouri River NRR, Gavins Point Dam, Nebraska.

44   International Peace Garden, Dunseith, North Dakota.

45   Elkhorn and Maltese Cross.

46   Minuteman Missile NHS, South Dakota.

47   Curecanti NRA, Colorado.

48   Colorado NM, Grand Junction, CO.

49   Glacier NP, Montana.

50   Waterton-Glacier International Peace Park.

51   Big Hole NB, Montana.

52   Correct answer is B.

53   Bighorn sheep.

54   Grant-Kohrs Ranch NHS, Deer Lodge, Montana.

55   Correct answer is A . . . the other member is Colorado.

56   Hovenweep NM, Colorado.
      Sidebar – When you visit plan a full "dry" day, for the site is
      remote and the roads are slick clay.

57   Timpanogos Cave NM, American Fork, Utah.

CHAPTER 10 –
NORTH ATLANTIC REGION
Questions and Answers

Purchased by Dutchman Peter Minuit from the Indians, for goods worth $24, New Amsterdam was transferred to the English and renamed New York.

The NPS North Atlantic Region consists of seven states – New Hampshire, Vermont, Connecticut, Massachusetts, Rhode Island, Maine and New York.

CHAPTER 10 –
NORTH ATLANTIC REGION
Questions

1   "Keep, ancient lands, your storied pomp!" cries she
With silent lips. "Give me your tired, your poor,
Your huddled masses yearning to breathe free,
The wretched refuse of your teeming shore.
Send these, the homeless, tempest-tosst to me.
I lift my lamp beside the golden door!"
       'The New Colossus', Emma Lazarus, 1883.

Seven rays project from the Statue of Liberty's crown. What do they represent?

2   There are twenty-five windows in Miss Liberty's crown. What do they represent?

3   Who is the French sculptor who designed the Statue of Liberty?

4   Emma Lazarus wrote her poem to raise funds to build the pedestal for the Statue of Liberty, which was a gift from France that came without one. To what does the title of her poem, <u>The New Colossus</u>, refer?

5   In the mid-nineteenth century, this NPS site was the whaling capital of the world. Until the discovery of petroleum, whale oil brought light to the world. This national historical park, one of our nation's newest – established in 1996 – was set aside to preserve America's maritime history. Name this park.

6   At the home of Ansley Wilcox in Buffalo, New York, this
       president took the oath of office to become America's 26th
       president. Who is the president and what NPS site
       commemorates that event?

7   Sagamore Hill in Oyster Bay, New York, was the Summer
       White House and residence of this president. Name the
       president. Hint: He was the first recipient of the Nobel Peace
       Prize.

8   "The British are coming", "The British are coming", shouted
       this patriotic American as he rode through the streets of what
       now is Boston National Historical Park. Name the great
       American who warned other Americans of the impending
       Revolutionary War danger.

9   "By the rude bridge that arched the flood,
                   Their flag to April's breeze unfurled,
               Here once the embattled farmers stood
                   And fired the shot heard round the world."
                       'Concord Hymn', Ralph Waldo Emerson.

       This national historic park commemorates the 19th-century
       literary achievements of such talented authors as Nathaniel
       Hawthorne and Louisa May Alcott, and preserves the wayside
       home in which they grew up. It also commemorates important
       sites of the American Revolution. Name the national historic
       park.

North Atlantic Region

10   What great American poet, himself a recipient of a NPS site,
       wrote the poem Paul Revere's Ride, a portion of which is
       printed below:

               "Listen, my children, and you shall hear
               Of the midnight ride of Paul Revere,
               On the eighteenth of April, in Seventy-five;
               Hardly a man is now alive
               Who remembers that famous day and year.

You know the rest. In the books you have read,
How the British Regulars fired and fled –
How the farmers gave them ball for ball,
From behind each fence and farmyard wall,
Chasing the redcoats down the lane,
Then crossing the fields to emerge again
Under the trees at the turn of the road,
And only stopping to fire and load.
So through the night rode Paul Revere . . .

Through all our history, to the last,
In the hour of darkness and peril and need,
The people will waken and listen to hear
The hurrying hoofbeats of that steed,
And the midnight message of Paul Revere."

11   This building was built on the original site of New York's old
      City Hall, where the first U.S. Congress met – NYC was the
      nation's capital until 1790. Name the building.

12   Eleanor Roosevelt moved out of her husband's birthplace and
      lifetime residence and into a nearby cottage, so that she could
      concentrate on her work. The lovely cottage estate came
      complete with pond and ducks. What is the name of the
      cottage, and for what organization did she work so hard?

ELEANOR ROOSEVELT

(1884-1962) Wife of Pres. Franklin
Roosevelt. Became a world leader
in civil and women's rights, labor
movements, and the U.N.

13   When do ducks at Eleanor's Cottage pond wake up in the
      morning?

14   As a gesture of friendship, Russian President Boris Yeltsin gave US President Bill Clinton a gift of Russian photos never before seen by the West. He presented the collection while visiting a presidential national historic site; the photo collection was added to the site's library. The photos were political in nature and quite moving. One such photo shows a young couple about to be hung by Stalin's commissars for refusing to renounce their Christian religion. Name the national historic site.

15   This president was born in New York City. The NPS manages his boyhood home. Name the president and the national historic site.

16   At this metropolitan site, unexpected varieties of wildlife can be viewed year round. Most notable are the 300 bird species, including sandpipers, waterfowl, herons, gulls, terns, warblers, geese, doves, woodpeckers and sparrows. In the spring, thousands of horseshoe crabs lay eggs in the sand. The summer treat is to watch the diamondback terrapin hatchlings scurry to the sea. In the fall, millions of migrating monarch butterflies emerge and delight viewers. Guess this national recreation area.

17   There are over 100 lighthouses along the coast of Maine, but only four within NPS property limits. Name any of the four Maine lighthouses the NPS has been tasked to protect, and the park at which they reside.

18   With Boston-whaler fishing boats offshore, lobster buoys bobbing in the surf, cages piled six-high on Bar Harbor piers and wharfs, and steam pouring out of roadside lobster vats, this national park and its suburbs capture the true spirit of New England. Name the salty old park.

19   This mountain, tallest on the eastern seaboard, is located at Acadia NP, Maine. Name the infamous mountain.

North Atlantic Region

20
     "It is the marriage of the soul with nature that
     makes the intellect fruitful and gives birth to imagination."
       Henry David Thoreau.

     "(The) quiet marriage of art and tended landscape that so
     clearly defined the American impressionist movement."
       Senator Joseph Lieberman.

Emerging first in Paris with such well known artists as Monet, Cezanne, Pissarro and Renoir, impressionism became a popular art form in late 19th.-century America. Artists drew (no pun intended) inspiration from the simplicity of everyday life; they painted in the great outdoors, working quickly to create an "impression" of what they saw in the ever-changing landscape. Thought by some to be America's greatest impressionistic artist, this man was often seen in his three-piece tweed suit, easel in a field, paint brush in one hand, palette in the other, painting the beautiful landscape surrounding his home. His home is now a national historic site. Name the site.

21
John D Rockefeller, Jr., donated 11,000 acres in 1913 to help establish a national park. He also built many miles of woodland paths for horse-drawn carriages only (cars still prohibited today). What park did he help create?

22
A 32-mile-long barrier island off Long Island has been a national seashore for 38 years. Dunes, grasses, shore-birds, horse crabs, a holly forest and a lighthouse are a few attractions. William Floyd Estate is nearby and worth a visit. Name the national seashore, and state for what Floyd is best known.

23
Name the War of 1812 fort built in Manhattan to protect NYC from the British.

24
On September 14, 1901 in the home of Ansley Wilcox, Buffalo, NY, this president took the oath of office and became the 26th President of the United States. Name the president.

North Atlantic Region

25 Women's Rights National Historical Park is the site of the first-ever Women's Rights Convention, held in 1848 at Wesleyan Chapel, Seneca Falls, NY. The convention, led by Elizabeth Cady Stanton, challenged America to social reforms, in every aspect of life, from voting and property rights, employment and educational opportunities, to divorce and custody laws. They defiantly declared that "all men **and women** are created equal". This declaration became the women's movement theme. As what was the declaration known?

PROGRESS OF WOMEN

This stamp recalls the first Women's Rights Convention, held in Seneca Falls, N.Y. in 1848, called by Elizabeth Stanton to fight for equal suffrage.

26 Revolutionary War battles were fought at this national historic park. The Neilson Farm House served as headquarters for Generals Poor, Learned and Benedict Arnold. Name this national historic park.

27 Along this trail can be seen Paul Revere House, Old North Church, Bunker Hill, Charlestown Navy Yard – home of the USS Constitution "Old Ironside" – Old State House, Old South Meeting House and Faneuil Hall. Name the trail and national historic park.

28 Boarding houses, cotton mills – one includes a weaving room with 88 operating looms – and turbines document a time of evolution in America, from the farm life to industrial city life. All are on display at this national historic park. Name it.

North Atlantic Region

29   This site preserves the home and office of one of America's premier landscape architects. He designed over 5,000 landscapes, including Golden Gate Park, Central Park and Yosemite Valley for the NPS. Name this talented architect and the historic site.

30   What important event in John Fitzgerald Kennedy's life took place at the national historic site in Brookline, MA?

31   Longfellow National Historic Site in Cambridge, Mass., is the home where Henry Wadsworth Longfellow raised his family and, incidentally, wrote poetry. He believed that, "Every home should have at least one Children's Hour every evening." Below is a fraction of his poem <u>Children's Hour</u>. Can you complete the missing words?

> "Between the dark and the daylight,
>   When the night is beginning to lower,
> Comes a pause in the day's occupations,
>   That is known as the Children's Hour.
>
> "I hear in the chamber above __
>   The patter of little ____,
> The sound of a door that is _____,
>   And voices soft and _____.
>
> "A whisper, and then a silence:
>   Yet I know by their merry ____
> They are plotting and planning together
>   To take me by _____.
>
> "A sudden rush from the stairway,
>   A sudden raid from the ____!
> By three doors left unguarded
>   They enter my castle ____!"

32   This site is home to the oldest African-American church in the United States. Name the national historic site.

33   Boston Harbor Islands National Recreation Area was established in 1996 by Congress, but nature established the islands long ago – from what?

34   Sandy beaches – 40 miles worth – dozens of fresh water ponds,
        acres of dunes, lighthouses and antique life-saving stations are
        a few things to keep you busy at this national seashore. Name
        the national seashore.

35   This site is birthplace, home and final resting place of two
        presidents. Name this national historic site.

36   What president was born in a brown-stone house in New York
        City that is today a NPS historic site?

37   This individual established Yellowstone National Park as
        America's first national park. He and his wife are buried at this
        NPS site. Name the national memorial.

38   Where did President Ulysses S. Grant work after he served two
        terms as president?

39   Alexander Hamilton, first U.S. Treasury Secretary, was fatally
        wounded in a duel with whom?

40   Alexander Hamilton, co-author of the 'Federalist Papers', lived
        for two years at Hamilton Grange, now a national memorial, on
        Manhattan's Upper West Side. Why did he call the home 'The
        Grange'?

41   East-central New York is the site of this presidential retirement
        home . . . it even has a flush toilet, new for its day. Name the
        national historic site.

42   Known for its 1665 cemetery, 18th-century church and the trial
        of John Peter Zenger and his victory for freedom of the press,
        this national historic site is located on the former village green
        of Eastchester, NY.
        Name this national historic site.

North Atlantic Region

43   This beautiful mansion on the Hudson River is surrounded by
      gently rolling country, charming springs and ponds, and elegant
      formal gardens. Its hardwood forest is a leaf-peepers delight in
      the fall. Period-furnished with original pieces from Europe, the
      mansion can be toured with a park ranger or self-guided.
      Name this national historic site.

44   The British built a fort at this site in 1758 to protect the Oneida
      Carry portage that linked the Atlantic Ocean and the Great
      Lakes. In 1776 the American colonists took posession of the
      fort, and fought the British throughout August 1777. Name this
      fort national monument.

45   In 1604-05, Pierre Dugan Sieur de Mons and a company of 78
      men attempted to establish a colony on what island? Hint: It
      shares an international coast.

46   President George Washington created the first national armory
      in 1794. Where is it?

47   The European settlement of Providence and the life and work
      of a well-known 17th-century statesman are commemorated at
      this national memorial. Name the national memorial.

48   This national park is unique because the federal government
      owns none of its land, and its untraditional assets are cities,
      towns, villages and one million people. Guess this national
      heritage corridor.

49   Known for its witch trials, this 18th-century trading port has an
      authentic wharf and West Indies goods store, the 17th-century
      Narbonne-Hale house, and other well- preserved historic
      buildings. Name this national historic site.

50   A blacksmith in 1646 was a talented, respected man . . . he was
      strong, versatile and creative. A blacksmith has worked this
      historic site for 350-plus years. Name this national historic site.

North Atlantic Region

51   This site is the home of the country's original conservationists, who wrote <u>Land and Nature</u> in 1864.
Name this national historic park.

52   President Teddy Roosevelt commissioned me to design the obverse side of the US quarter. I designed a magnificent eagle. I chose the eagle because, unlike Ben Franklin, I thought the turkey inappropriate. I own a 150-acre home that features my studio, gardens and artwork. Although I have many favorites, if I had to choose my favorite artwork, I would nominate my full-size, bronze sculpture of Lt. Colonel Robert G. Shaw, Harvard graduate and twice-wounded civil war veteran, who volunteered to lead the all-black 54th Massachusetts Regiment to charge Fort Wagner, at the entrance to Charleston harbor, SC. Lt-Col. Shaw was killed in the first attempt . . . 300 of the 600 black soldiers were also killed. They, however, captured Fort Wagner on the third attempt. My statue took me ten years to sculpture and shows Shaw on horseback with ten soldiers marching faithfully beside him. (This extremely remarkable sculpture can be viewed at the National Gallery of Art – West Wing, WDC.) The NPS is managing my home. I loved my gardens . . . come grade me as a gardener. Who am I?

North Atlantic Region

CHAPTER 10 –
NORTH ATLANTIC REGION
Answers

1   The seven rays represent the seven continents, i.e., Europe, Asia, Africa, North America, South America, Australia and Antarctica.

2   The windows represent the 25 precious gems of the world.

3   French sculptor, Barroldi.

4   The Colossus of Rhodes, one of the seven great wonders of the world, which was a giant statue of the sun god Helios that had overlooked the Greek city's harbor.
Sidebar – At the Empire State Building, ground floor, visitors waiting for an elevator to the top can enjoy paintings, complete with information placards, of each of the seven great wonders of the ancient world.)

5   New Bedford Whaling NHP, New Bedford, Massachusetts.

6   President Theodore Roosevelt; Theodore Roosevelt Inaugural NHS.

7   President Theodore Roosevelt; Sagamore Hill NHS is a simple but elegant home where many of Teddy's hunting trophies and scientific collections are on display.

8   Paul Revere.

9   Minuteman NHP, Concord, Lincoln and Lexington,
        Massachusetts.

10   Answer is Henry Wadsworth Longfellow.

11   Federal Hall, NYC; now protected by the NPS . . . yes, you can
        get a Passport cancellation here.

12   Val-Kill Cottage, Eleanor Roosevelt NHS, Hyde Park, NY; she
        was a major contributor to the United Nations.

13   At the quake of dawn.

14   Home of Franklin Delano Roosevelt NHS, Hyde Park, NY.

15   Theodore Roosevelt, 26th US President; Theodore Roosevelt
        Birthplace NHS, New York City, NY.

16   Gateway NRA, New York City, NY.
        Sidebar – Gateway has two units; the Staten Island unit, where
        you are most likely to view monarch butterflies, and the
        Jamaica Bay – Breezy Point unit where you find the most
        birds.

17   Bass Harbor, Bear Harbor, Baker Island and Egg Rock Island
        Lighthouse; all at Acadia NP, Bar Harbor, Maine.

18   Acadia NP, Bar Harbor, Maine.

19   Cadillac Mountain.

20   Weir Farm NHS, Branchville, Connecticut.

21   Acadia NP, Bar Harbor, Maine.

22   Fire Island NS, Mastic, New York; signer of the Declaration of
        Independence.

North Atlantic Region

23   Castle Clinton NM.

24   Theodore Roosevelt Inaugural NHS

25   Declaration of Sentiments.

26   Saratoga NHP, New York.

27   Freedom Trail at Boston NHP.

28   Lowell NHP, Massachusetts.

29   Frederick Law Olmsted NHS, Brookline, Massachusetts.

30   His birth.

31   First verse = me, feet, opened, sweet
Second verse = eyes, surprise
Third verse = hall, wall.

32   Boston African American National Historic Site, Mass.

33   Glacial drumlins.

34   Cape Cod NS, Mass.

35   Adams NHS, Quincy, Mass.

36   Theodore Roosevelt, 26th US President – Theodore Roosevelt
Birthplace NHS, NY.

37   Grant's Tomb – General Grant National Memorial, NYC.

38   Wall Street, NYC.

39   Aaron Burr, on July 11, 1804.

40   It was named after the family ancestral home in Scotland.

41   Martin Van Buren NHS, Kinderhook, NY.

42   Saint Paul's Church NHS, Mount Vernon, NY.

43   Vanderbilt Mansion NHS, Hyde Park, NY.

44   Fort Stanwix NM, Rome, NY.

45   Saint Croix Island International Historic Site; Calais, Maine.
        Sidebar – Since Jamestown was founded in 1607 and Plymouth
        in 1620, Saint Croix is the earliest European settlement on the
        North Atlantic coast.

46   Springfield Armory NHS, Massachusetts.

47   Roger Williams N MEM, Providence, Rhode Island.

48   Blackstone River Valley NHC, Woonsocket, Rhode Island.

49   Salem Maritime NHS, Massachusetts.

50   Saugus Iron Works NHS, Massachusetts.

51   Marsh-Billings NHP, Woodstock, Vermont.

52   Augustus Saint-Gaudens . . . the NPS manages his estate, Saint-
        Gaudens National Historic Site, near Cornish, New Hampshire.

North Atlantic Region

CHAPTER 11 –
MID-ATLANTIC REGION
Questions and Answers

PHILADELPHIA

GETTYSBURG ADDRESS

Commemorating 85th anniversary of immortal speech delivered by Pres. Lincoln at dedication of cemetery on this hollowed battlefield.

APPOMATTOX

Commemorating end of the bloody War between the States (1861-65).

YORKTOWN

Blockaded by a fleet at sea and on American and French army ashore, Cornwallis surrendered at Yorktown in 1781, ending the American Revolution.

BATTLE OF THE WILDERNESS

A Civil War battle between the forces of Generals Grant and Lee May 5-6, 1864, in Spotsylvania County, Va.

Mid-Atlantic Region

The NPS Mid-Atlantic Region consists of six states – Pennsylvania, New Jersey, Delaware, Maryland, West Virginia and Virginia.

CHAPTER 11 –
MID-ATLANTIC REGION
Questions

1   I am a 200-plus year-old home. My owner was, first and foremost, a loving, caring husband, second, a signer of the Declaration of Independence, and, lastly, a tobacco farmer. What am I?

2   "He has lost his left arm, I have lost my right arm", said General Robert E. Lee when learning his top general lost his left arm, after being shot by friendly forces. Without his troops' knowledge, this general went out at night to survey enemy lines secretly. When he returned to camp,, his own troops shot him three times in the left arm and hand. That evening his mangled arm was amputated; eight days later he died of pneumonia. Upon learning of the general's death, Lee remarked, "Any victory is dearly bought that deprives us of the services of the general even for a short time." What general is this, and at what battle did this accident take place?

3   The NPS is managing the estate of this Civil War general, which overlooks Arlington National Cemetery, the Potomac River and WDC. Whose home is it?

4

> "If I can stop one heart from breaking,
> I shall not live in vain;
> If I can ease one life the aching,
> Or cool one pain,
> Or help one fainting robin
> Unto his nest again,
> I shall not live in vain."
>> 'If I Can Stop One Heart from Breaking', Emily Dickinson.

This woman founded the American Red Cross and was known throughout the country as the Angel of the Battlefield. Her 38-room house served as the first Red Cross headquarters and is now a NPS historic site. Name this NPS NHS.

5
"Again at the hospital I see the horrid results
of every battle. Men mutilated in every shape
conceivable, groaning, begging for assistance
and gasping in death. Many of our wounded
will have to lie all night in that horrid swamp.
It being impossible to find them and carry them
out on the narrow foot bridge . . . Many have had
their heads propped up to keep them from drowning."
      Diary of Lt Col Oscar I. Jackson – 63rd Ohio Infantry
      after battle of Rivers Bridge, SC.

Clara Barton helped Jean Henry Dunant establish the
International Red Cross. Jean's idea was to build an
international team to help soldiers on the battlefield, regardless
of their nationality, race or religion. Clara expanded on Jean's
idea by adding an 'American Amendment', as it came to be
known, to the charter of the International Red Cross. What was
the American Amendment?

CLARA BARTON

Civil War nurse, founder and first
president of The American National Red
Cross, responsible for Pres. Arthur's
signing of Geneva Convention.

6
Francis Scott Key witnessed the British shelling of this
nationally important 18th–century fort. It so inspired him that
he wrote a song. Name the song and the fort.

7
John Brown and his band of raiders captured the Federal
arsenal at Harpers Ferry, West Virginia (Now Harpers Ferry
National Historic Park) in 1859. He had a wild scheme to arm
the slaves and start a revolt in the south. Under the leadership

Mid-Atlantic Region

of a West Point graduate, the US Army stormed the arsenal, arrested Brown, quickly tried him for treason, and hanged him. What US Army colonel led the attack and captured Brown?

8   After testing rocks in its riverbed, geologists have determined that this national river is the second-oldest river in the world, the oldest being the Nile River in Egypt. Name the national river. Hint: Its name is misleading, opposing and contrary.

9   General Robert E. Lee surrendered to General Ulysses S. Grant at this national historic park, ending the Civil War. Name the national historic park.

10 Green space remarkably close to two metropolitan areas is the main value and attraction of this park. A pleasurable retreat from hectic urban life, this park is home to red fox, raccoons, hardwood forest, wildflowers and all manner of bird-life. Name the park.

11   "Part of the valley is God's,
            And part is man's.
            The river course laid out
            A thousand years ago.
            The canals ten years back."
                'Joliet', Carl Sandburg.

    Strolling along this park's tow-path, you have the quiet waters of the canal on one side, and the swifter currents of the Potomac River, on its way over Great Falls, on the other. Tow-path is shared: bikers and hikers, roller bladers and joggers, historians and naturalists, photographers and lovers, turtles and dragonflies, herons and butterflies – all out to enjoy nature. Name this national historical park.

12 The Mid-Atlantic Region is a stronghold of this black-capped gull. Name the gull. Hint: It is very funny.

13 A place for long walks on the beach, for dreaming or viewing wildlife, this barrier island national seashore is home to wild ponies. From April through the summer expect to see thousands

Mid-Atlantic Region

of herons, egrets, terns and gulls feeding on the bayside. In the fall, plan on watching monarch butterflies feeding on wildflowers. Flocks of snow geese winter here. Name this lovely national seashore.

14   "Now we are engaged in a great civil war
testing whether this nation, or any nation
so conceived and so dedicated, can long endure."
       President Abraham Lincoln, November 19, 1863.

Site of the largest civil-war battle ever fought in the Western Hemisphere, bloodiest battle of the American Civil War, with 51,000 killed, wounded or captured, this site saw Union troops turn back the wecond, and final, invasion of the north by the Confederates. Name this national military park.

15   "High Water Mark of the Confederacy" is a term used to describe what American Battle?

16   French artist Paul Philippoteaux was tasked by the US government to prepare a 360-ft long, circular oil-on-canvas painting to reflect the fury of "Pickett's Charge", the final Confederate assault of a famous battle of 1863. What is the name of this art piece, and where can it be found?

17   "The [Civil] war being at an end . . . I believe it to be the duty of every one to unite in restoration of the country, and the establishment of peace and harmony . . . " Which great Civil War personality said that?
A = Abraham Lincoln
B = Ulysses S. Grant
C = Robert E. Lee
D = John Sherman

18   What person of the following distinguished group was not a field nurse in the Civil War?
A. Walt Whitman
B. Clara Barton
C. Sally Pompkins
D. Elmer Ellsworth

Mid-Atlantic Region

19   "The splash and crank of the turning water wheel and the
       swirling roar of the furnace 'blast' never stopped. By day, black
       charcoal dust swirled from the furnace and blanketed the whole
       village; by night, only a flickering red glow lit the sky."
       NPS – TwHP

This national historic site provides a glimpse into the iron and
steel industry, which played a major role in America's leap to
being an industrial power. Name this national historic site.

20   "River take me away,
       in the springtime, changing and free.
       In the moonlight, wild and so free,
       you rolling old river, you changing old river,
       let you and me river go down to the sea." Bill Stains.

Set aside for the people actively to enjoy, this national river
sustains kayaking, canoeing, white water rafting, horseback
riding, hiking, fishing and hunting. Name this national river.
Hint: Blue Heron scenic railroad.

21   Which river is not a national river managed by the NPS in West
       Virginia?
       A.   Bluestone River
       B.   Gauley River
       C.   Devils Gorge River
       D.   New River

22   Twenty-nine miles of scenic parkway connect two of the
       world's busiest, most prestigious metropolitan areas. The NPS
       is tasked with protecting and preserving this green-belt. Pierre
       l'Enfant, the 18th–19th century city planner, had his hand in
       this pie. Name this scenic commute. Hint: No trucks allowed!

23   In the wake of the War of 1812, when Washington was burned
       by the British, some new ideas on how to protect Washington,
       DC were drastically needed. This fort rose to the forefront and
       subsequently saw the installation of 24-pound cannons, and
       eventually rifled cannons. Many Civil War-era living-history
       programs are enacted here. Park interpreters, dressed in
       authentic 19th-century military uniforms, recreate life on the
       fort for visitors. Name this national fort park.

Mid-Atlantic Region

24   What symbol best declares "that all men are created equal and endowed with certain unalienable rights", as Thomas Jefferson so eloquently put it? And at what national historic park can it be found?

25   General Grant, with the Union Army at his side, besieged this Confederate city for nine months. The siege severed railroad lines and kept General Lee from getting much-needed supplies . . . seven days after the siege Lee surrendered to Grant. Name the city and its national battlefield.

26   With its clean water, good fishing, and bald-eagle watching, Middle and Upper Delaware Scenic and Recreational Rivers are enjoyed regularly by residents in two states. What are they?

27   Two Civil War clashes between the Confederate and Union forces were fought here. Nearly 900 men lost their lives in July 1861, and 3,300 died during three days of battle in August 1862. The park is 26 miles west of Washington, DC. Name the national battlefield park.

28   If America had royalty, in a similar manner to the British, one might expect this park to be named for a member of our royal family. Name this national forest park.

29   Between 1861 and 1865, Union troops repeatedly tried to capture this southern city. Name the city and famous national battlefield.

30   Skyline Drive, which crests the Blue Ridge Mountains, is the best reason to visit this national park. Name the national park.

31   If you enjoy an open-air performing arts pavilion with lots of room to stretch out on the grass and munch fried chicken, sip lemonade and listen to a full course orchestra, this NPS site is for you. Name it!

32   Where was George Washington born?

Mid-Atlantic Region

33   A great American educator, orator and presidential advisor was born, reared and emancipated from slavery at this former plantation. Name this national monument. Hint: He taught at Tuskegee Institute, Alabama.

34   The NPS commemorates an African-American civic leader who rose to prominence after the Civil War and is recognized as America's first woman bank president. Name this national historic site.

35   The NPS protects and manages a green belt with historic significance in Washington, DC. Name the parkway and the presidential grove of trees that can be found there.

36   Steamtown National Historic Site is the former yard for what main-line steam railroad?

37   Blood-red windows line the private library of this author's eerie home. Only the strong of heart should visit on Halloween. Name this national historic site.

38   In the winter of 1844, a destitute, shabby young man and his wife called upon his old boss at the offices of Graham's Magazine in New York. He submitted a poem he had written. It was rejected, but instead his boss passed the hat, collected $15.00 from his former colleagues and presented it to him as a gift. The author was Edgar Allan Poe. What was the poem?

39   If you enjoy seeing mangled bodies wrapped around fence posts, homes splintered into pieces no bigger than kindling, debris of all types scattered in every direction, cars stacked on top of cars, and general disarray, this is the national memorial for you. Name the devastating national memorial.

40   George Washington and his Continental Army were encamped here from December 19, 1777 to June 19, 1978 during the American Revolution. Name this national historic park.

Mid-Atlantic Region

41   While Washington and the troops were camped out for the
        winter, this Polish-born engineer and patriot roomed in
        Philadelphia. A national memorial has been dedicated to him in
        Philadelphia.
        Name it. Hint: A bridge in Philadelphia bears his name.

42   *The Historic Triangle*, also called the *Triple Shrines*, at
        Colonial National Historical Park refers to three historic areas.
        Which area is considered part of the *Historic Triangle*?
        A. Jamestown – site of the initial landing of English
            settlers and 1st Settlement;
        B. Williamsburg – 18th-century capital and center of
            activity;
        C. Yorktown – site of the conclusive battle of the
            Revolutionary War;
        D. All of the above.

43   Camp David, the presidential retreat, is located within the
        confluence of this national park. Name the park.

44   What did engineers use to lift canal boats, loaded on railroad
        flat-cars, over the Allegheny (Mountain) Portage?

45   Before United Flight 93 crashed on September 11, 2001 in a
        field in Shanksville, Pennsylvania, Todd Beamer led a group of
        heroic Americans in overcoming the terrorists and diverting
        their evil mission. What were Todd's now-famous last words in
        defense of freedom?

46   This park was established to protect the river view across from
        George Washington's home, Mount Vernon. It is exactly the
        way things were in George's day. You may tour a working 18th-
        century farm on site. Name this park.

47   Hampton Mansion was the largest home in the United States
        when it was finished. It was a vast agricultural and commercial
        estate. Hampton National Historic Site formal gardens,
        outbuildings and mansion can be toured today. When was the
        mansion built?

Mid-Atlantic Region

48   Known as the "Battle That Saved Washington", on July 9, 1864, this battle was the last Confederate attempt to carry the Civil War into the North. Name this national battlefield.

49   On these fields, a quarter-mile stretch known as "Bloody Lane", 5,600 Union and Confederate soldiers lost their lives in three hours, in what is now considered the bloodiest single day of battle in American history. Name this national battlefield.

50   Charles de Gaulle and Nikita Khrushchev visited this US president at his home, which is now a national historic site. Name this national historic site.

51   Fort Necessity, Pennsylvania, was used by George Washington during what war, in what year?

52   Friendship Hill estate belonged to what 19th-century statesman?

53   The treaty that ended the American Revolutionary War and, hence, Britain's colonial period is known as?

54   In May 1607, the first British settlers arrived in America at what is now Virginia and called the area Jamestown in honor of King James I. They arrived in the Susan Constant, the Godspeed and what other ship?

55   What was the capital of Virginia during the British colonial period of 1607 through 1699?

56   Between 1607 and 1624, approximately 5,000 setters came to the Virginia colonies from Britain. How many survived?

57   George Washington slept here . . . he also commanded the Continental Army from a home here during the harsh winters of 1779 and '80 when many soldiers were dying from starvation and hyperthermia, and others mutinied. Name this national historic park.

Mid-Atlantic Region

58   Glenmont was home and laboratory to what great American inventor?

59   New Jersey has a scenic recreational river that drains 300 miles of pristine wetlands in its Pineland Reserve. Name this scenic and recreational river.

CHAPTER 11 –
MID-ATLANTIC REGION
Answers

1   Thomas Stone House NHP, Tobacco, Maryland.

2   General Stonewall Jackson; Battle of Chancellorsville –
        Chancellorsville is now a separate unit of Fredericksburg and
        Spotsylvania National Military Park, Virginia.

3   Arlington House; the Robert E. Lee Memorial is the home Lee
        lived in for 30 years.

4   Clara Barton NHS, Glen Echo, Maryland.

5   Clara lobbied Congress for funding and campaigned to add an
        American Amendment that authorized the International Red
        Cross, and gave it financial strength, to help victims of all
        calamities that befall mankind, e.g., earthquakes, floods,
        tornadoes, forest fires and epidemics.

6   Star Spangled Banner – which became the United States
        national anthem; Fort McHenry NM, Baltimore, MD.

7   US Army Colonel Robert E. Lee,
        Sidebar – Lee was a Federal army officer before the Southern
        States seceded from the Union. After the Southern secession,
        Lee changed sides and commanded the Confederate Army.

8   New River Gorge NR, West Virginia.

9   Appomattox Court House, Appomattox, Virginia.

10   Greenbelt Park, Maryland.

11   Chesapeake and Ohio Canal NHP, Washington DC and
        Maryland.

12   The laughing gull.

13   Assategue Island NS; Maryland and Virginia.

14   Gettysburg NMP, Gettysburg, Pennsylvania.

15   Battle of Gettysburg; Gettysburg NMP, Gettysburg,
        Pennsylvania.

16   "Battle of Gettysburg" Cyclorama; new visitor center,
        Gettysburg NMP, Gettysburg, Pennsylvania;
        Sidebar – A cyclorama was a popular form of entertainment in
        the late 19th century. It consisted of a colossal painting, formed
        to fit inside a circular auditorium, enhanced with real brush,
        fenceposts, wagons and a few life-sized figures.
            The surrounded spectator gets the three-dimensional effect of
        being involved in the action. Philippoteaux painted the first of
        four "Battle of Gettysburg" cycloramas for the City of Chicago
        in 1882. The second was painted for the City of Boston. The
        original was purchased by the NPS. After extensive restoration,
        it is now on display at Gettysburg NMP.

BATTLE OF GETTYSBURG

In the Civil War's most decisive battle,
Meade's Army of the Potomac defeated
Lee's Army of Northern Virginia. From
then on South was doomed.

17   Correct answer is C, Robert E. Lee.

Mid-Atlantic Region

18   Correct answer is D.
        Sidebar - Ellsworth was a 24 year old Union colonel who led
        the famous Zouaves Battalion with colorful green uniforms he
        designed. After capturing Alexander, Virginia, Ellsworth ran up
        to the roof of a hotel and cut down a Confederate flag; while
        descending the stairs he was shot dead by a southern
        sympathizer.
            After visiting his wounded brother, Walt Whitman became a
        male nurse. Sally Pompkins did for the South what Clara
        Barton did for the North.

19   Hopewell Furnace NHS Elverson, Pennsylvania.

20   Big South Fork NRRA Kentucky/Tennessee.

21   Correct answer is C.

22   Baltimore-Washington Parkway.

23   Fort Washington Park, Maryland.

24   The Liberty Bell – Independence Hall NHP.

25   Petersburg NB, Virginia.

26   New Jersey and Pennsylvania.

27   Manassas NBP, Virginia.

28   Prince William Forest Park, Virginia.

29   Richmond NBP, Virginia.

30   Shenandoah NP, Virginia.

31   Wolf Trap Farm Park for the Performing Arts, Virginia.

32   George Washington Birthplace NM, of course. Colonial Beach,
        Virginia.

Mid-Atlantic Region

33   Booker T. Washington NM, Roanoke, Virginia.

34   Maggie L. Walker NHS Richmond, Virginia.

35   George Washington Memorial Parkway – Lyndon B. Johnson NHP.

36   Delaware, Lackawanna & Western Railroad.

37   Edgar Allan Poe NHS, Philadelphia, Pennsylvania.

38   The Raven.

39   Johnstown Flood N MEM, St. Michael, Pennsylvania.

40   Valley Forge NHP, Pennsylvania.

41   Thaddeus Kosciuszko N MEM.

42   Correct answer is D.

43   Catoctin Mountain Park.

44   Ten inclined planes.

45   Let's Roll!

46   Piscataway Park, Accokeek, Maryland.

47   1790.

48   Monocacy NB, Frederick, Maryland.

49   Antietam NB, Maryland.

50   Eisenhower NHS, Gettysburg, Pennsylvania.

51   French and Indian War, 1754.

52   Albert Gallatin, Secretary of the Treasury from 1801 to 1814.

Mid-Atlantic Region

53   The Treaty of Paris.

54   The Discovery.

55   Jamestown – now part of Colonial National Historical Park.

56   700 survived; 300 returned either ill or discouraged; and 4,000 died from starvation, Indian attack or disease.

57   Morristown NHP, New Jersey.

58   Thomas Edison NHS, West Orange, New Jersey.

59   Great Egg Harbor SRR.

Mid-Atlantic Region

CHAPTER 12 -
NATIONAL HISTORIC TRAILS

PONY EXPRESS

Tribute to brave men who carried mail, costing $5 an oz., between Sacramento, Cal. and St. Joseph, Mo. 1900 mile ride took ten days.

LEWIS & CLARK EXPEDITION

This expedition made the first continental crossing within the U.S., reaching the Pacific Ocean, and made scientific collections and observations

AMERICAN INDIAN

Joseph, wise and humane chief of the Nez Perce (pierced nose) Indians.

CORONADO EXPEDITION

Coronado (1500-1554), a grandee and conquistador of New Spain, found the Grand Canyon and explored vast areas of southwestern United States.

NPS Trails include: Oregon NHT, Pony Express NHT, Mormon Pioneer NHT, Ice Age NHT, Nez Perce NHT, Juan Bautista de Anza NHT, Lewis and Clark NHT, Trail of Tears NHT, Pacific Crest NST, Selma to Montgomery NHT, Santa Fe NHT, Iditarod Trail Sled Dog Race NHT, Appalachian NST, Natchez Trace NST, Potomac Heritage NST, Florida NST, Overmountain Victory NHT, California NHT, North Country NST and Continental Divide NST.

National Trails System

CHAPTER 12
NATIONAL HISTORIC TRAILS
Questions

There are currently 7 scenic and 13 historic national trails.

1 "Married soldiers and officers are to be sought with
the idea that having transported their wives and
children to the port of San Francisco, they may
immediately form a colony there."
Antonio Maria Bucareli y Ursua, December 27, 1774.

In the winter of 1775-76, under this commander's direction, a
240-member Spanish expedition including wives and children,
340 horses, 165 pack mules and 300 beef cattle, traveled 1,200
miles from the Mexican capital of Sonora to the port of San
Francisco. This colony became the first European settlers of
San Francisco, and marked the furthest point north the Spanish
migrated into North America. Name the national historic trail
that is named after the Spanish commander.

2 President Thomas Jefferson purchased Louisiana from
Napoleon in 1800, thereby doubling the size of the United
States. From that day on, America stretched from the East coast
clear across the continent to the West coast. But nobody knew
for certain what lay west beyond the Mighty Mississippi.
Jefferson tasked two men to conduct an expedition to find out.
The trail they took, to and fro, is now a national historic trail.
They traveled 8,000 miles over a period of two years, four
months and ten days, in what today encompasses 11 States.
Name this national historic trail.

National Trails System

12 - 2

3

"The great severity of the weather, and
. . . the difficulty of crossing the river
during many days of running ice, all
combined to delay our departure,
though for several days the bridge of
ice across the Mississippi greatly
facilitated our crossing."
  Brigham Young, February 1846.

"In advance of us, at a great distance
can be seen the outlines of mountains
loftier than any we have yet seen . . .
their summits . . . covered with snow."
  Horace Whitney, June 1847.

". . . and beholding in a moment such an
extensive scenery opened before us, we
could not refrain from a shout of joy
which almost involuntarily escaped
from our lips the moment this grand
and lovely scenery was within our view."
  Orson Pratt, July 1847.

Persecuted because of their religious belief, in our country
which was founded on religious freedom for all, this group of
people migrated west from Nauvoo, Illinois in 1846-47. The
NPS in its fine, attractive and free brochure states, "(Their
journey) was not entirely voluntary; but to maintain a religious
and cultural identity it was necessary to find an isolated area
where they could permanently settle and practice their religion
in peace. This was a movement of an entire people, an entire
religion, an entire culture driven by religious fervor and
determination." Name the national historic trail these
courageous people followed west, which is named after them.

4   Across the plains, over the Continental Divide, through the dry
deserts they came in droves. This 2,170-mile trail was used by
400,000 people in the 1840's. The Whitmans and Spaldings
used this trail to go west and start their ill-fated Indian Mission.
Albert Bierstadt's painting 'The Emigrants Crossing' (National
Cowboy Hall of Fame, Oklahoma City) and William Henry
Jackson's painting 'Wagon Train at Independence Rock'

National Trails System

(Denver Public Library) best portray the feeling and mood of this trail. Name this national historic trail. Hint: This trail crosses the Continental Divide by following an old Crow Indian path.

5   Overmountain Victory National Historic Trail was authorized by Congress to commemorate what important event in American History?

   A.   Patriot Militia – Mountain Men – marched over the mountains through Virginia, Tennessee, and North Carolina to Kings Mountain, South Carolina where they defeated the superior British-Loyalist army.

   B.   Pioneer settlers' covered-wagon crossing of the Appalachian Mountains, led by Jim Bowie.

   C.   General Sherman's march from Maryland across the Appalachian Mountains to Charleston, South Carolina, to retake Charleston for the Union.

   D.   General Robert E. Lee's march to Gettysburg.

6   Part of a vast trade network, this trail linked Europe, New York, and St. Louis with Santa Fe and Mexico. Name this national historic trail.

7   North Cascades NP, Mt. Rainer NP, Crater Lake NP, Lassen Volcanic NP, Yosemite NP, Devils Postpile NM, Sequoia – Kings Canyon NP's, are all NPS sites that are connected by this 2,650 mile national scenic trail. Name this national scenic trail.

8   "You asked us to throw off the hunter and warrior state – we did so. You asked us to form a republican government – we did so. You asked us to cultivate the earth and learn the mechanical arts – we did so. You asked us to cast away our idols and worship your God – we did so."
              John Ridge, 1832, Cherokee spokesperson.

That same year, 1832, the U.S. Supreme Court ruled that the laws one State made against the Cherokee were unconstitutional. The atrocious laws included: Cherokee government now null and void; Cherokees were not allowed to

National Trails System

mine; Cherokees were not to hold meetings or testify against whites in court. Nevertheless, the president refused to enforce the rulings of the Supreme Court and went so far as to say it was "absurd" to think that a sovereign nation could operate independently within the United States. He further stated, "(the Cherokees) had neither the intelligence, the industry, the moral habits nor the desire of improvement which are essential to any favorable change in their condition." What State made these awful laws, and which president failed to uphold the ruling of the highest court in our land?

9   During the winter of 1838-39 the U.S. Cavalry, empowered by the Indian Removal Act, forced-marched tens of thousands of Cherokee Indians off their lands in Tennessee, North Carolina, Georgia and Alabama, and walked them out west to Oklahoma. One-third died of starvation and exposure on the way. The NPS memorializes their unjust suffering with placards along the trail. Name this national historic trail.

10 To satisfy the U.S. government that the Cherokee would improve their own lot and govern themselves, this Cherokee chief invented a written language that, in 1821, all Cherokee learned to read and write. He and many of his braves served the U.S. government in the War of 1812 against the British. Name this dedicated native American. Hint: A tree specie in California bears his name.

11 The completion of the Overland Telegraph in October 1861, between Sacramento, CA, and Salt Lake, UT, put out of business use what national historic trail?

12   "I, _____, do hereby swear, before the Great and Living God, that during my engagement, and while I am an employee of Russell, Majors and Waddell, I will, under no circumstances, use profane language; that I will drink no intoxicating liquors; that I will not quarrel or fight with any other employee of the firm, and that in every respect I will conduct myself honestly, be faithful in my duties, and so direct all my acts as to win the confidence of my employers. So help me God."

National Trails System

Employees of what famous government-financed organization were required to take the above pledge of allegiance? Hint: Speed is an American virtue!

13　　　"FAREWELL PONY: Our little friend, the pony, is to run no more . . . Farewell and forever, thou staunch, wilderness-over-coming, swift-footed messenger. For the good thou hast done we praise thee; and, having run thy race, and accomplished all that was hoped for and expected, we can part with thy services without regret . . . "
　　　　　Sacramento Bee editorial, October 26, 1861.

How long was the Pony Express in operation?

14　　White Bird, Clearwater, Fort Fizzle, Big Hole, Birch Creek, Camas Meadows, Canyon Creek, Cow Island and Bears Paw are, for the most part, campsites and/or battlefields located on what tragic national historic trail?

15　　General Howard dispatched Companies F and H of the U.S. Army 1st Cavalry, under Captain Perry, to put down an Indian uprising. On June 17, 1877, Captain Perry and his cavalry met the Nez Perce Indians at White Bird Canyon and a battle resulted. Which side was victorious?

16　　Medgar Evers shot and killed because he helped blacks register to vote, two students killed trying to enroll James Meredith in the University of Mississippi, four young girls are killed when their church is bombed in Birmingham, Rosa Parks refuses to be bullied into giving up her seat on a bus for a white person, state troopers and deputized white citizens spray blacks with tear gas and beat them with nightsticks – captured on news film and broadcast all over the nation billed as "Bloody Sunday" – these are some of the events that triggered an historic march led by Martin Luther King, Jr. This national historic trail commemorates that march. Name this national historic trail.

17　　"Alaska, where men are men and women win __??__ ." What do women win that inspired this slogan to appear on T-shirts all across the state?

National Trails System

18   <u>Part A:</u>
With what did Libby Riddles fortify herself, to have enough energy to withstand the severe snowstorms and below-zero temperatures, to win the Iditarod Trail Sled Dog Race?
<u>Part B:</u>
What unconventional action did Libby take to help insure her victory?

19   What was the purpose of the original Iditarod National Historic Trail, how many miles is it? How many miles is the Iditarod Trail Sled Dog Race?

20   What is the Iditarod trail named for, and what does the word Iditarod mean?

21   The highest elevation along the Iditarod Trail is:
A = 5,554 ft.   B = 3,350 ft.   C = 11,762 ft.   D = 9,881 ft.

22   To qualify to participate in 'The Last Great Race' – the Iditarod Trail Sled Dog Race – a musher must have at least the minimum number of dogs, and no more than the maximum number allowed. What are the minimum and maximum sled dog limits?

23   The first to win 'The Last Great Race' was Dick Wilmarth in 1973, who completed the race in 20 days. He started with the ceiling limit of 16 dogs and completed the race with 10 dogs. Since that first successful race, a sled dog race has been run each year beginning on the first Saturday of March. What is the fastest time the Iditarod Trail was blazed and when was this record set?

24   "I wish California had sunk into the ocean before I ever heard of it . . . That desert has played hell with us."
                James Wilkins, pioneer, 1849.

Half-frozen and trapped by early winter snow, a party of emigrant pioneers was stranded for the winter of 1846-47. Some starved to death, others resorted to cannibalism. Name the party and the national historic trail they followed.

National Trails System

25 What was the main attraction that caused a mad stampede across the California National Historic Trail in 1848?

26 Ice Age National Scenic Trail winds over 500 plus miles of glacial moraine in what State?

27 Which of the following statements best describes a moraine:
   A. A zone of snow accumulation during the ice age;
   B. Sea floors spreading apart at rift lines in the ocean basin during the ice age;
   C. A shallow sea that spread over much of the area as a result of ice age meltdown;
   D. An area covered by rock, sand and other debris carried down and deposited by a receding glacier during the ice age meltdown.

28 What was the nation's first designated national scenic trail?

29 The Appalachian Scenic Trail is 2,160 miles long, takes all summer to hike, begins in Georgia and passes through 14 states before ending in Maine. The NPS, via volunteers, maintains trails and campsites along the way that were originally built by the Civil Conservation Corps in the 1930's. Name the 12 other states the trail passes through.

30 Choctaw, Chickasaw, Creek, Cherokee and another 'author-disguised' (for fear of give-away) native American tribe used this trail to assist, entertain, educate and basically live life for several centuries. Name this national scenic trail. Hint: Trace European explorers.

31 Florida National Scenic Trail is just that, a place to stroll and enjoy some pretty special scenery. Where does it begin and end?

32 Runoff runs west, runoff runs east, in fact, runoff runs on either side of this national scenic trail as it travels the Rocky Mountains from Canada to Mexico. Name this national scenic trail.

33   North Country National Scenic Trail runs east and west for
      1,400 miles through what states?

34   Mount Vernon – George and Martha Washington's home –
      Chesapeake and Ohio Canal, Georgetown, Watergate, Roosevelt
      Island are a few of the wonderful places to explore as you hike
      this interesting and well-laid-out hiking-biking national scenic
      trail. Name it.

National Trails System

CHAPTER 12
NATIONAL HISTORIC TRAILS
Answers

1   Juan Bautista de Anza NHT.

2   Lewis and Clark NHT.
        Sidebar – The trail begins at the Jefferson National Expansion
        Memorial, St. Louis, Missouri and ends at Fort Clatsop
        National Memorial, Oregon. Paved roadway parallels most of
        the trail, with many roadside pull-outs for viewing the
        landscape and reading well-laid-out, colorful information
        boards.

3   Mormon Pioneer Trail NHT – Illinois to Utah.

4   Oregon NHT, Missouri to Oregon.

5   Correct answer is A.

6   The Santa Fe Trail NHT.

7   Pacific Crest NST, West Coast, Mexico to Canada.

8   Georgia – Andrew Jackson, 7th U.S. president.

9   Trail of Tears.

10   Sequoyah

11   Pony Express NHT, Missouri to California

12   Riders of the Pony Express

13   It was short-lived, it lasted a brief 18 months.

National Trails System

14   Nez Perce NHT, Oregon to Montana.

15   The Nez Perce.
        Sidebar – Under a flag of truce, six Nez Perces approached
        Captain Perry and his troops; they were mistakenly fired upon
        by an inexperienced recruit. During the ensuing battle 34
        cavalry soldiers lost their lives, no Nez Perce were killed. Thus
        began the flight of the Nez Perce along the infamous Nez Perce
        NHT, and their eventual capture at Bear Paw Mountains.

16   Selma to Montgomery NHT, Alabama.

17   The Iditarod Trail Sled Dog Race – which is a 1,000 mile run
        between Anchorage and Nome; Libby Riddles won the Iditarod
        in 1985, Susan Butcher won in 1986, '87, '88, and '90.

18   Part A = Norwegian chocolate and seal oil;
        Part B = She snuck out of camp in the middle of the night and
        continued her journey, while the competition slept. Good for
        her!

19   Iditarod NHT commemorates the original Seward to Nome
        Mail Trail and gold-rush paths, used to support the gold
        prospectors in the 1910s and 1920s; it is approximately 2,450
        miles. The dog-sled race, only a portion of the original gold
        prospectors' trail, is run from Anchorage to Nome, Alaska, and
        covers about 1,000 miles.

20   It is named after the gold prospector's ghost town of Iditarod,
        which, in turn, is named for the Iditarod River and means
        "distant place", but has now found itself synonymous with
        strength and endurance.

21   Correct answer is B – the elevation of Rainy Point.

22   Mushers must have at least five dogs to proceed, and are
        allowed as many as 16 dogs.

National Trails System

23   Each year the Iditarod Trail Sled Dog Race is completed faster and faster; in 2002 the race was completed by Martin Buser in 8 days, 22 hours, 46 minutes and 2 seconds . . . race record-keeping is getting hi-tech . . . the dogs have come a long way – no pun intended.

24   Donner Party, California NHT.

25   Discovery of gold at Sutter's Mill, California.

26   Wisconsin.

27   Correct answer is D.

28   Appalachian NST – Georgia to Maine in 1968.

29   North Carolina, Tennessee, Virginia, West Virginia, Maryland, Pennsylvania, New Jersey, New York, Connecticut, Massachusetts, Vermont and New Hampshire.

30   Natchez Trace NST Mississippi, Alabama and Tennessee.

31   Florida NST begins at Big Cypress N PRES and meanders the Kissimmee Prairie through national and state forests before coming to an end at the Gulf islands.

32   Continental Divide NST, Golden, Colorado.

33   From New York to North Dakota.

34   Potomac Heritage NST, Virginia, Washington, D.C., Maryland and south Pennsylvania.

National Trails System

APPENDIX A
National Park System

Type of Designation	Total Units
National Battlefields	11
National Battlefield Parks	3
National Battlefield Site	1
National Military Parks	9
National Historical Parks	40
National Historic Sites	77
International Historic Sites	1
National Lakeshores	4
National Memorial	30
National Monuments	75
National Parks	56
National Parkways	4
National Preserves	17
National Reserves	2
National Recreation Areas	18
National Rivers	5
National Wild and Scenic Rivers & Riverways	10
National Scenic Trails	3
National Seashores	10
Units Without Designation	11

TOTAL UNITS = 387

Appendix A – A Complete
Listing of All 388 NPS Sites

NATIONAL BATTLEFIELDS (11)

1. Antietam, Maryland
2. Big Hole, Montana
3. Cowpens, South Carolina
4. Fort Donelson, Tennessee-Kentucky
5. Fort Necessity, Pennsylvania
6. Monocacy, Maryland
7. Moores Creek, North Carolina
8. Petersburg, Virginia
9. Stones River, Tennessee
10. Tupelo, Mississippi
11. Wilson's Creek, Missouri

NATIONAL BATTLEFIELD PARKS (3)

1. Kennesaw Mountain, Georgia
2. Manassas, Virginia
3. Richmond, Virginia

NATIONAL BATTLEFIELD SITE (1)

Brices Cross Roads, Mississippi

NATIONAL MILITARY PARKS (9)

1. Chickamauga and Chattanooga, Georgia-Tennessee
2. Fredericksburg and Spotsylvania County Battlefields Memorial, Virginia
3. Gettysburg, Pennsylvania
4. Guilford Courthouse, North Carolina
5. Horseshoe Bend, Alabama
6. Kings Mountain, South Carolina
7. Pea Ridge, Arkansas
8. Shiloh, Tennessee
9. Vicksburg, Mississippi

NATIONAL HISTORICAL PARKS (40)

1. Adams, Massachusetts
2. Appomattox Court House, Virginia
3. Boston, Massachusetts
4. Cane River Creole NHP and Heritage Area, Louisiana
5. Chaco Culture, New Mexico
6. Chesapeake and Ohio Canal, Maryland-West Virginia-District of Columbia
7. Colonial, Virginia
8. Cumberland Gap, Kentucky-Tennessee-Virginia
9. Dayton Aviation Heritage, Ohio
10. George Rogers Clark, Indiana
11. Harpers Ferry, West Virginia-Maryland
12. Hopewell Culture, Ohio
13. Independence, Pennsylvania
14. Jean Lafitte NHP and Preserve, Louisiana
15. Kalaupapa, Hawaii
16. Kaloko-Honokohau, Hawaii
17. Keweenaw, Michigan
18. Klondike Gold Rush, Alaska-Washington
19. Lowell, Massachusetts
20. Lyndon B. Johnson, Texas
21. Marsh-Billings-Rockefeller, Vermont
22. Minute Man, Massachusetts
23. Morristown, New Jersey
24. Natchez, Mississippi
25. New Bedford Whaling, Massachusetts
26. New Orleans Jazz, Louisiana
27. Nez Perce, Idaho
28. Pecos, New Mexico
29. Pu'uhonua o Honaunau, Hawaii (formerly, City of Refuge)
30. Rosie the Riveter/World War II Home Front, Richmond, California
31. Salt River Bay NHP & Ecological Preserve, St. Croix, V.I.
32. San Antonio Missions, Texas
33. San Francisco Maritime, California
34. San Juan Island, Washington
35. Saratoga, New York
36. Sitka, Alaska
37. Tumacacori, Arizona

38. Valley Forge, Pennsylvania
39. War in the Pacific, Guam
40. Women's Rights, New York

NATIONAL HISTORIC SITES (77)

1. Abraham Lincoln Birthplace, Kentucky
2. Allegheny Portage Railroad, Pennsylvania
3. Andersonville, Georgia
4. Andrew Johnson, Tennessee
5. Bent's Old Fort, Colorado
6. Boston African American, Massachusetts
7. Brown v. Board of Education, Kansas
8. Carl Sandburg Home, North Carolina
9. Charles Pinckney, South Carolina
10. Christiansted, Virgin Islands
11. Clara Barton, Maryland
12. Edgar Allan Poe, Pennsylvania
13. Edison, New Jersey
14. Eisenhower, Pennsylvania
15. Eleanor Roosevelt, New York
16. Eugene O'Neill, California
17. First Ladies, Canton, Ohio
18. Ford's Theatre, District of Columbia
19. Fort Bowie, Arizona
20. Fort Davis, Texas
21. Fort Laramie, Wyoming
22. Fort Larned, Kansas
23. Fort Point, California
24. Fort Raleigh, North Carolina
25. Fort Scott, Kansas
26. Fort Smith, Arkansas-Oklahoma
27. Fort Union Trading Post, Montana-North Dakota
28. Fort Vancouver, Washington
29. Frederick Douglass, District of Columbia
30. Frederick Law Olmsted, Massachusetts
31. Friendship Hill, Pennsylvania
32. Golden Spike, Utah
33. Grant-Kohrs Ranch, Montana
34. Hampton, Maryland

35. Harry S Truman, Missouri
36. Herbert Hoover, Iowa
37. Home of Franklin D. Roosevelt, New York
38. Hopewell Furnace, Pennsylvania
39. Hubbell Trading Post, Arizona
40. James A. Garfield, Ohio
41. Jimmy Carter, Georgia
42. John Fitzgerald Kennedy, Massachusetts
43. John Muir, California
44. Knife River Indian Villages, North Dakota
45. Lincoln Home, Illinois
46. Little Rock Central High School, Arkansas
47. Longfellow, Massachusetts
48. Maggie L. Walker, Virginia
49. Manzanar, California
50. Martin Luther King, Jr., Georgia
51. Martin Van Buren, New York
52. Mary McLeod Bethune Council House, District of Columbia
53. Minuteman Missile, South Dakota
54. Nicodemus, Kansas
55. Ninety Six, South Carolina
56. Palo Alto Battlefield, Texas
57. Pennsylvania Avenue, District of Columbia
58. Puukohola Heiau, Hawaii
59. Sagamore Hill, New York
60. Saint-Gaudens, New Hampshire
61. Saint Paul's Church, New York
62. Salem Maritime, Massachusetts
63. San Juan, Puerto Rico
64. Saugus Iron Works, Massachusetts
65. Springfield Armory, Massachusetts
66. Steamtown, Pennsylvania
67. Theodore Roosevelt Birthplace, New York
68. Theodore Roosevelt Inaugural, New York
69. Thomas Stone, Maryland
70. Tuskegee Airmen, Alabama
71. Tuskegee Institute, Alabama
72. Ulysses S. Grant, Missouri
73. Vanderbilt Mansion, New York
74. Washita Battlefield, Oklahoma

Appendix A – A Complete
Listing of All 388 NPS Sites

75. Weir Farm, Connecticut
76. Whitman Mission, Washington
77. William Howard Taft, Ohio

INTERNATIONAL HISTORIC SITES (1)
Saint Croix Island, Maine

NATIONAL LAKESHORES (4)
1. Apostle Islands, Wisconsin
2. Indiana Dunes, Indiana
3. Pictured Rocks, Michigan
4. Sleeping Bear Dunes, Michigan

NATIONAL MEMORIALS (30)
1. Arkansas Post, Arkansas
2. Arlington House, The Robert E. Lee Memorial, Virginia
3. Chamizal, Texas
4. Coronado, Arizona
5. De Soto, Florida
6. Federal Hall, New York
7. Fort Caroline, Florida
8. Fort Clatsop, Oregon
9. Franklin Delano Roosevelt Memorial, District of Columbia
10. General Grant, New York
11. Hamilton Grange, New York
12. Jefferson National Expansion Memorial, Illinois-Missouri
13. Korean War Veterans, District of Columbia
14. Johnstown Flood, Pennsylvania
15. Lincoln Boyhood, Indiana
16. Lincoln Memorial, District of Columbia
17. Lyndon Baines Johnson Memorial Grove on the Potomac, District of Columbia
18. Mount Rushmore, South Dakota
19. Oklahoma City, Oklahoma
20. Perry's Victory and International Peace Memorial, Ohio
21. Roger Williams, Rhode Island
22. Thaddeus Kosciuszko, Pennsylvania

23. Theodore Roosevelt Island, District of Columbia
24. Thomas Jefferson Memorial, District of Columbia
25. USS Arizona Memorial, Hawaii
26. Vietnam Veterans Memorial, District of Columbia
27. Washington Monument, District of Columbia
28. Wright Brothers, North Carolina
29. Flight 93 Memorial Shanksville, Pennsylvania
30. World War II Memorial, Washington DC

NATIONAL MONUMENTS (75)
1. Agate Fossil Beds, Nebraska
2. Alibates Flint Quarries, Texas
3. Aniakchak, Alaska
4. Aztec Ruins, New Mexico
5. Bandelier, New Mexico
6. Booker T. Washington, Virginia
7. Buck Island Reef, Virgin Islands
8. Cabrillo, California
9. Canyon de Chelly, Arizona
10. Cape Krusenstern, Alaska
11. Capulin Volcano, New Mexico
12. Casa Grande Ruins, Arizona
13. Castillo de San Marcos, Florida
14. Castle Clinton, New York
15. Cedar Breaks, Utah
16. Chiricahua, Arizona
17. Colorado, Colorado
18. Congaree Swamp, South Carolina
19. Craters of the Moon, Idaho
20. Devils Postpile, California
21. Devils Tower, Wyoming
22. Dinosaur, Colorado-Utah
23. Effigy Mounds, Iowa
24. El Malpais, New Mexico
25. El Morro, New Mexico
26. Fort Matanzas, Florida
27. Florissant Fossil Beds, Colorado
28. Fort Frederica, Georgia
29. Fort McHenry NM and Historic Shrine, Maryland Updated:

30. Fort Pulaski, Georgia
31. Fort Stanwix, New York
32. Fort Sumter, South Carolina
33. Fort Union, New Mexico
34. Fossil Butte, Wyoming
35. George Washington Birthplace, Virginia
36. George Washington Carver, Missouri
37. Gila Cliff Dwellings, New Mexico
38. Governor's Island, Governor's Island, New York
39. Grand Portage, Minnesota
40. Great Sand Dunes NM & Preserve, Colorado
41. Hagerman Fossil Beds, Idaho
42. Hohokam Pima, Arizona
43. Homestead NM of America, Nebraska
44. Hovenweep, Colorado-Utah
45. Jewel Cave, South Dakota
46. John Day Fossil Beds, Oregon
47. Lava Beds, California
48. Little Bighorn Battlefield, Montana
49. Minidoka Internment, S. Central, Idaho
50. Montezuma Castle, Arizona
51. Muir Woods, California
52. Natural Bridges, Utah
53. Navajo, Arizona
54. Ocmulgee, Georgia
55. Oregon Caves, Oregon
56. Organ Pipe Cactus, Arizona
57. Petroglyph, New Mexico
58. Pinnacles, California
59. Pipe Spring, Arizona
60. Pipestone, Minnesota
61. Poverty Point, Louisiana
62. Rainbow Bridge, Utah
63. Russell Cave, Alabama
64. Salinas Pueblo Missions, New Mexico
65. Scotts Bluff, Nebraska
66. Statue of Liberty, New York-New Jersey
67. Sunset Crater Volcano, Arizona
68. Timpanogos Cave, Utah
69. Tonto, Arizona

70. Tuzigoot, Arizona
71. The Virgin Islands Coral Reef, St. John, U.S. Virgin Islands
72. Walnut Canyon, Arizona
73. White Sands, New Mexico
74. Wupatki, Arizona
75. Yucca House, Colorado

NATIONAL PARKS (56)

1. Acadia, Maine
2. Arches, Utah
3. Badlands, South Dakota
4. Big Bend, Texas
5. Biscayne, Florida
6. Black Canyon of the Gunnison
7. Bryce Canyon, Utah
8. Canyonlands, Utah
9. Capitol Reef, Utah
10. Carlsbad Caverns, New Mexico
11. Channel Islands, California
12. Crater Lake, Oregon
13. Cuyahoga Valley, Ohio
14. Death Valley, California-Nevada
15. Denali, Alaska
16. Dry Tortugas, Florida
17. Everglades, Florida
18. Gates of the Arctic, Alaska
19. Glacier Bay, Alaska
20. Glacier, Montana
21. Grand Canyon, Arizona
22. Grand Teton, Wyoming
23. Great Basin, Nevada
24. Great Smoky Mountains, Tennessee-North Carolina
25. Guadalupe Mountains, Texas
26. Haleakala, Hawaii
27. Hawaii Volcanoes, Hawaii
28. Hot Springs, Arkansas
29. Isle Royale, Michigan
30. Joshua Tree, California
31. Katmai, Alaska

32. Kenai Fjords, Alaska
33. Kings Canyon, California
34. Kobuk Valley, Alaska
35. Lake Clark, Alaska
36. Lassen Volcanic, California
37. Mammoth Cave, Kentucky
38. Mesa Verde, Colorado
39. Mount Rainier, Washington
40. North Cascades, Washington
41. Olympic, Washington
42. Petrified Forest, Arizona
43. Redwood, California
44. Rocky Mountain, Colorado
45. Saguaro, Arizona
46. "NP of" Samoa, American Samoa
47. Sequoia, California
48. Shenandoah, Virginia
49. Theodore Roosevelt, North Dakota
50. Virgin Islands, Virgin Islands
51. Voyageurs, Minnesota
52. Wind Cave, South Dakota
53. Wrangell-St. Elias, Alaska
54. Yellowstone, Wyoming-Montana-Idaho
55. Yosemite, California
56. Zion, Utah

PARKWAYS (4)
1. Blue Ridge Parkway, North Carolina
2. George Washington Memorial Parkway, Virginia
3. John D. Rockefeller Jr., Memorial Parkway, Wyoming
4. Natchez Trace Parkway, Mississippi

NATIONAL PRESERVES (17)
1. Aniakchak, Alaska
2. Bering Land Bridge, Alaska
3. Big Cypress, Florida
4. Big Thicket, Texas
5. Denali, Alaska

6. Gates of the Arctic, Alaska
7. Glacier Bay, Alaska
8. Great Sand Dunes, Colorado
9. Katmai, Alaska
10. Lake Clark, Alaska
11. Little River Canyon, Alabama
12. Mojave, California
13. Noatak, Alaska
14. Tallgrass Prairie, Kansas
15. Timucuan Ecological and Historic, Florida
16. Wrangell-St. Elias, Alaska
17. Yukon-Charley Rivers, Alaska

NATIONAL RESERVES (2)
1. City of Rocks, Idaho
2. Ebey's Landing NH Reserve, Washington

NATIONAL RECREATION AREAS (18)
1. Amistad, Texas
2. Bighorn Canyon, Montana-Wyoming
3. Boston Harbor Islands, Massachusetts
4. Chattahoochee River, Georgia
5. Chickasaw, Oklahoma
6. Curecanti, Colorado
7. Delaware Water Gap, Pennsylvania-New Jersey
8. Gateway, New York-New Jersey
9. Gauley River, West Virginia
10. Glen Canyon, Arizona-Utah
11. Golden Gate, California
12. Lake Chelan, Washington
13. Lake Mead, Nevada-Arizona
14. Lake Meredith, Texas
15. Lake Roosevelt (formerly Coulee Dam)
16. Ross Lake, Washington
17. Santa Monica Mountains, California
18. *Whiskeytown Unit, Whiskeytown-Shasta-Trinity, California

---

*Administered under cooperative agreements with other Federal agencies; remaining units managed by Forest Service.

NATIONAL RIVERS (5)
1. Big South Fork National River and Recreation Area, Tennessee-Kentucky
2. Buffalo National River, Arkansas
3. New River Gorge National River, West Virginia
4. Mississippi National River and Recreation Areas, Minnesota
5. Ozark National Scenic Riverways, Missouri

NATIONAL WILD AND SCENIC RIVERS (10)
1. Alagnak Wild River, Alaska
2. Bluestone National Scenic River, West Virginia
3. Delaware National Scenic River, Pennsylvania-New Jersey-New York
4. Great Egg Harbor National Scenic and Recreational River, New Jersey
5. Missouri National Recreation River, Nebraska-South Dakota
6. Niobrara National Scenic Riverway, Nebraska-South Dakota
7. Obed Wild and Scenic River, Tennessee
8. Rio Grande Wild and Scenic River, Texas
9. Saint Croix National Scenic Riverway, Minnesota-Wisconsin
10. Upper Delaware Scenic and Recreation River, New York-Pennsylvania

NATIONAL SCENIC TRAILS (3)
1. Appalachian National Scenic Trail, Maine to Georgia
2. Natchez Trace National Scenic Trail, Mississippi-Tennessee
3. Potomac Heritage National Scenic Trail, Virginia-Pennsylvania

NATIONAL SEASHORES (10)
1. Assateague Island, Maryland-Virginia
2. Canaveral, Florida
3. Cape Cod, Massachusetts
4. Cape Hatteras, North Carolina
5. Cape Lookout, North Carolina
6. Cumberland Island, Georgia
7. Fire Island, New York

8. Gulf Islands, Florida-Mississippi
9. Padre Island, Texas
10. Point Reyes, California

Units Without Designation (11)
1. Catoctin Mountain Park, Maryland
2. Constitution Gardens, District of Columbia
3. Fort Washington Park, Maryland
4. Greenbelt Park, Maryland
5. National Capital Parks, District of Columbia
6. National Mall, District of Columbia
7. Piscataway Park, Maryland
8. Prince William Forest Park, Virginia
9. Rock Creek Park, District of Columbia
10. White House, District of Columbia
11. Wolf Trap Farm Park for the Performing Arts, Virginia

AFFILIATED AREAS (27)
1. Aleutian World War II National Historic Area, (Unalaska), Alaska
2. American Memorial Park, Saipan
3. Benjamin Franklin National Memorial, Pennsylvania
4. Blackstone River Valley National Heritage Corridor, Massachusetts-Rhode Island
5. Chicago Portage National Historic Site, Illinois
6. Chimney Rock National Historic Site, Nebraska
7. David Berger National Memorial, Ohio
8. Delaware & Lehigh Navigation Canal National Heritage Corridor, Pennsylvania
9. Fallen Timbers Battlefield, Ohio
10. Father Marquette National Memorial, Michigan
11. Gloria Dei (Old Swedes') Church National Historic Site, Pennsylvania
12. Green Springs National Historic Landmark District, Virginia
13. Historic Camden Revolutionary War Site, South Carolina
14. Ice Age National Scenic Trail, Wisconsin
15. Ice Age National Scientific Reserve, Wisconsin
16. Ilinois and Michigan Canal National Heritage Corridor, Illinois
17. International Peace Garden, North Dakota-Manitoba

18. Jamestown National Historic Site, Virginia
19. McLoughlin House National Historic Site, Oregon
20. Lewis and Clark National Historic Trail, Missouri to Oregon
21. Pinelands National Reserve, Pennsylvania
22. Port Chicago Naval Magazine National Memorial, California
23. Quinebaug and Shetucket River Valley National Heritage Corridor, Connecticut
24. Roosevelt Campobello International Park, New Brunswick, Canada
25. Sewall-Belmont House National Historic Site, District of Columbia
26. Thomas Cole National Historic Site, New York
27. Touro Synagogue National Historic Site, Rhode Island

About the Author:

Photos from top left clockwise are: Kenneth hiking Bartlett Cove Glacier Bay NP; Glacier Bay with Mount Fairweather in the background (taken at midnight during white-nights) and park concession tour boat – Spirit of Adventure – in the foreground; and about to canoe Katmai NP, Alaska.

Mr. Brophy is a civil-structural engineer, float pilot and 'Birder'. America's National Parks: How Well Do You Know Them? is his first book, albeit he has been researching it for the past 17-years – a true labor of love. He has visited 362 of America's 388 national park sites and has enjoyed each and every visit. Besides visiting all 50 states, he has traveled to 77 countries and made sure to visit at least one national park in each. He is working on his next book, 'World's Greatest Parks'. He has a home in South Paris, Maine, but is currently building schools in Iraq.

Two man Kayak trip to Muir Inlet Glacier Bay NP with friend David D

If you would like to contribute a question and answer for inclusion in the next edition of America's National Parks: How Well Do You Know Them?, please send your question and answer to the author at <u>Kbrophy@msn.com</u>. All reasonable questions will be considered.